Balance

A powerful guide to overc[...]nic attacks by bringing the brain, body [...] spirit back into balance. Coming to you from personal experience.

Brought to you by Habitat for Wellness.

Taleen Keuftedjian (Author)

ISBN: 978-1-7370644-1-1

Check out habitatforwellness.com to read blogs on mental wellness, with an emphasis on WHOLE-BODY health. Habitat for Wellness is here to help others live a healthier, happier, anxiety-free life!

habitatforwellness.com

Take a picture of the QR code below to read more articles on mental wellness

Introduction

I'm a believer in oneness rather than separation, which is why I write this book with humbleness and humility. I reveal my vulnerabilities and struggles that I've gone through in life, so that I can connect with you on a personal level. This way, I can get you to identify and overcome your own emotional trauma that led up to where you are today. When I was younger, anxiety was stigmatized as being "uncool" or the complete opposite of being "chill." This made it tougher to talk about or deal with, so I'm hoping this book will shed light on the realness of anxiety.

My first experience with anxiety started when I was 9 years old. It continued to haunt me for 18 years and would morph like a chameleon into different forms of anxiety, like hypochondria, social anxiety, panic attacks, and phobias. As a little girl, I was infused with fear, robbed of my childhood joy and innocence. I thought it was something I was going to have to live with for the rest of my life, until I hit rock bottom one day at 27 years old. After experiencing the worst panic attack of my life, I decided enough is enough. I was going to do everything possible to balance out my bossy brain. I sometimes refer to anxiety as my bossy brain, because that's exactly what it is. It dominates your time, demands your attention, dictates your life, and drives you NUTS!

I completely understand how you might be feeling right now because I was there once before. And I really had it bad. That feeling of being uncomfortable in your skin, wanting to escape your body, but having nowhere to run to. You might be feeling like you're alone right now, surrounded by people who don't understand what you are going through. But the truth is, there are many people in the world experiencing the same things you are. Many people are prisoners of their own bossy brain, but what they don't know is that this isn't who they are at the core. This book will help you discover your full potential, while exposing the real you, which I'm sure is pretty freaking awesome! Freedom from anxiety is possible, it just takes knowledge, effort, and a whole lot of dedication. You need to balance your body and heal from within in order to be whole again. You're going to get through this and become a stronger person as a result of it.

Ok, I'm not promising that your anxiety will never come back, especially if you're hungover as hell, smoke a cigarette, and drink a strong cup of coffee while running on 2 hours of sleep. But after incorporating the concepts in this book, your whole perspective on life will change, and these toxic habits will become a thing of the past. You will learn to love and respect your body enough to say NO to toxicity. The bossy brain will no longer control you, taking your brain from bossy to bliss.

Over the last 10 years, I've gained a lot of knowledge regarding mental health, the brain body connection, and nutrition plans, for a healthy functioning brain. I've been anxiety free for over 10 years now as a result of many of the concepts that I'll be introducing you to in this book. My goal is to educate you about the potential root causes of anxiety, so I can get you to think about where your anxiety might be stemming from. Anxiety is a symptom of an imbalance within the body, rather than a disease in itself. For this reason, we must look at it from a holistic perspective or else we will never actually cure anxiety, we will only be managing the symptoms.

In this book I incorporate concepts relating to the brain, body, and spirit, as I believe all of these are interconnected. An imbalance in one of these components can manifest itself into an array of issues. First, we need to learn how to eliminate stress, so that we can eliminate the stress hormones running through our body. Most people don't realize that it's these excessive stress hormones that are continuously triggering the "fight or flight" response. I emphasize the importance of releasing stagnant emotional trauma, learning to live in the present moment, and ditching the ego. Then I'll introduce you to different techniques and technologies which can be very effective in helping you gain control of your bossy brain. There is also a huge connection between the brain and gut, called the gut-brain axis, which is why I encourage you to focus on detoxing and nourishing your body. We need to balance out the chemicals within our body in order to tame our brain, and this all begins with the gut. Finally, maintaining genuine happiness must come from within, rather than external factors, which is why we must discover who we really are at the core.

So, find your authentic self by embracing spiritual freedom, and allowing the universe to deliver whatever it is your heart desires. Just trust that there's a reason you picked up this book and embark on this journey with me!

Chapter 1: Introduction

My Story

It all started in 1993 when I was 9 years old. My mom came to pick me up from school and told me I had to go to the doctor to get a checkup. I asked her why. She told me that I needed to get a checkup once a year so that the doctor can catch any diseases early on. So, here's how my child brain interpreted this as. "Wait … I can get diseases?! And the doctor will tell me when I get a disease?! And I can die from these diseases?! Oh, hell no …" And this is when my bossy brain took over.

So now I was terrified of doctors, associating them with death and disease. In addition, I started thinking I had every disease in the book, which is when my hypochondria began. I became obsessed and couldn't even hear the word "disease" without getting a rush of fear run through my body. As a young child, I would eat tons of fruits and veggies in hopes that this would cure or prevent diseases. I would thoroughly inspect my body each day to see if any new marks or lumps had developed. It became an obsession of mine, which I kept to myself for the longest time. I suffered with this horrible thought that I would one day succumb to one of these deadly diseases, and never make it to my 16th birthday. I prayed, and prayed, and prayed. "God, I just want to be able to drive a car. Please let me live to 16!"

In my mind, I could not tell a soul, because if I did, they would make me go to the doctor where I would get my death sentence. Therefore, I harbored this secret for more than 10 years. The paranoia got so out of control that I thought I had HIV even though I was a virgin. How crazy is that? How could it be possible? Well … my bossy brain convinced me that it was definitely a possibility. I would look at the people around me and admire them for being disease free. In my mind, they were all happy, oblivious, and carefree, while I sat there disease ridden waiting for my impending death.

The birth of my ego. It was 1996, and I was 11 years old. It was my 6th grade school presentation. I was walking on stage to present my project on the Bahamas in front of about 100 people. The Beach Boys' song Kokomo was playing, and I was dancing over to the podium feeling like a rock star. Suddenly, the song dissipated, and it was time for me to present my project. I froze! "Ugh ugh ugh … Wait! What happened? I know all the words. Why am I going blank now? What the hell! Wait … why is my heart racing? Why can't I breathe? What's happening?" And so it began. I experienced my first panic attack ever and it happened in front of the whole school AND their parents. How humiliating! Can I just disappear so I never have to see these people again?

Ego is defined as a sense of self-esteem, self-importance, and personal identity. Ego is commonly only associated with someone who is confident or full of themselves, but this is not necessarily the case. Someone who is shy can have a larger ego than the more confident person. In fact, everyone has an ego, and that moment during the school presentation is when my ego came into full force. My childhood innocence was officially gone. I was now so concerned with being judged by others that I just threw my hands up and said screw it! I'd rather be a rebel than a school nerd.

This was my way of distracting people from my deepest secrets and insecurities. I would rebel against my teachers or anyone else that was an authoritarian figure in my life, thinking they were the ones causing me these feelings of insecurity, loneliness, and unworthiness. After years of personal growth and ego awareness, I can now look back with a fresh pair of eyes. It was my ego that made me feel those subpar feelings, and no one else. My ego was causing me to seclude myself from everybody around me. This created a sense of deep loneliness in my adolescent years, despite being surrounded by friends and family. I was a victim of my bossy brain.

Later that year, my 19-year-old cousin who I hadn't seen for years showed up at my doorstep. I was bursting with excitement and admiration at the fact that she was beautiful, popular, smart, and basically had it all! But most important, she was disease free! Lucky her. I could only wish to be like her one day. She took me to the coolest spots in San Francisco, invited her friends over, and would dance around to Madonna, singing "Like a Virgin" with her hairbrush as her microphone. "Oh my god, my cousin is the best! I love her! I want to be just like her!" After about a week, she went back to Las Vegas which is where she lived at the time. A few days later, I went on my Outdoor Ed school trip for a few days. Little did I know that I was going to come back home to the devastating news that would change my life forever. My cousin had a brain aneurysm, was in a coma, and I was told her chances of survival were very slim. Later that evening my dearest cousin passed away at only 19 years old. I was crushed. I was heartbroken. "How could this be? How could someone so energetic, beautiful, radiant, vibrant, and young, die so suddenly. How could this be? How? She was healthy! I saw her 2 weeks ago!" Well, this was when my panic attacks took a whole new turn.

If my cousin can die suddenly, not knowing that there was something wrong with her, then that can happen to me too! This is when I developed a fear of fainting and falling to my inevitable death. During these imaginary fainting episodes, my heart would pound out of my chest, my breathing would become shallow, and my body temperature would shoot up. My bossy brain would convince me by saying, "See … I'm fainting. I'm fainting. Look what's happening! My vitals are changing because I'm fainting. Oh wait, now I can't breathe. I'm going to stop breathing, and I'm going to die. Someone help me!" This would happen over, and over, and over again. Each episode I experienced was just as convincing as the first one. It's amazing that I could never look back at the prior day and say, "Hey … this happened yesterday, and I didn't faint. Maybe this could be the same thing and I won't faint again? Nope … It's happening, and this is the time that I'm actually going to faint and die." Oh man, I was so utterly convinced!

Not only did I now have recurring random panic attacks, but I also had a fear of vacationing because I thought I would come back to some other devastating news. Who's next? My mom, my dad, my brother? My thought process was beyond irrational, yet my bossy brain had me so convinced.

So now I'm 14 years old with a serious case of hypochondria, panic attacks, and a huge fear of losing someone else around me. My ego was officially out of control as I entered high school. I started smoking cigarettes, drinking alcohol, and doing anything else that would label me as a rebel. You might be asking yourself why the heck would I be doing the things that cause disease, when I'm terrified of diseases in the first place. Well, my ego took over and it seemed being cool was more important than taming my bossy brain. At this time, I started to realize that alcohol would ease my anxiety in the moment, while making it 100 times worse the next day. I would just deal with the terrors of my anxious hangover as long as I got to party with my friends the night before. I got to the point where I was partying by night, and anxiety ridden by day. I struggled with this lifestyle well into my mid-20's.

At 27 years old, I met who I thought was the man of my dreams. He was good looking, a musician, an intellectual, and a personal trainer. We only dated for about a year, but within that year, I had given up cigarettes and alcohol to be with him. One day, we went on a trip with my friends to Santa Cruz, and it was my first time getting wasted in a long time. It seemed like the greatest day ever since my friends were finally meeting my boyfriend and we could all party it up together. Well, the next morning I woke up with only 2 hours of sleep and a huge haze of anxiety. I finally mustered up some courage to meet my friends to have breakfast. I grabbed a strong cup of coffee and smoked the cigarette that would change my life forever. My anxiety went from 10 to 1000 in about a minute. I literally thought I lost my mind. I was a walking ball of anxiety. My eyes were closing, I couldn't breathe, my heart was pounding out of my chest, I was sweating profusely, pacing back and forth throughout the streets, feeling like I was taken out of reality. Of course, my "awesome" boyfriend had no idea what I was going through, nor did he even try to help me get through it, which made it all even worse. I just wanted out!

The haze of anxiety lasted weeks, as my body was in a continuous "fight or flight" state, in which stress hormones were continuously being pumped through my body. The cloud of ongoing fear and brain fog left me debilitated, unable to leave the house. I told my boyfriend that I needed some time to myself, which of course he couldn't understand, so he ended up breaking up with me. Drinking coffee would exasperate the haze even more and I couldn't even bear to smoke a cigarette. I never thought a panic attack could last for weeks on end, but it did. It didn't seem like things could get any worse.

At the time, I was working at a big advertising agency that was crowded with people and loud noise. I remember the music blasting, people talking, bright lights above me, and having a busy day of work ahead of me. All of a sudden the panic started to hit me, and I finally had a complete breakdown. I ran into my boss's office to tell her I was leaving, and I didn't know when I would be back. I then made my way out to the busy streets of San Francisco thinking it would make it better, but it didn't. Thousands of people, busy traffic, street vendors, honking horns, and homeless people asking for money. It felt like insanity. I somehow made my way down into the subway station to get my ass home. I finally got to my car and made it halfway home before it started to hit me again. I shut off the radio, parked the car, and busted into tears. I asked myself, "Am I losing my mind? What is happening to me?" Eventually, I was able to call my dad to pick me up. My dad has never experienced anxiety himself, so he could not relate to what I was going through. However, he has a nurturing vibe to him that makes me feel protected and secure. This sense of security is exactly what I needed in that chaotic moment. As soon as he picked me up, I felt an immediate sense of relief. He took me to my parent's house, and I went straight to the bedroom to relax. The weirdest full body vibrating sensations were coming over me as my nervous system started to disarm itself. At this moment, I didn't think I would ever be normal again. I decided I needed a break from the world for a while, so I moved back in with my parents.

My anxiety was extremely crippling, and I could not see the light at the end of the tunnel. It was so hard for me to get anything done, and I felt like my mind was in a constant haze. I started seeing a therapist that did absolutely nothing for me. He actually told me he didn't think he could help me any further, and to not waste my money anymore. I started taking anxiety medication for the first time, which seemed to help me gain control, although it came at a price. I found myself lacking interest, passion, and nothing seemed to excite me anymore. I knew I needed to drop the meds as soon as possible without causing a relapse.

I decided it was finally time to shut my bossy brain up and go to the doctors to get a full physical. I was so desperate for sanity that I didn't even care what the doctor was going to tell me, I just needed to know. A few days later I got my results and heard the best news of my life. My blood tests were normal, and I was disease free. I was now more determined than ever to take control of my life, and nothing was going to stop me. I began to slowly wean off the anxiety meds and started to focus on educating myself on health, nutrition, and the gut-brain connection. I would read any books or articles that involved nutrition, disease, and mental health. I became fascinated with health-related documentaries and researching emerging ideas on the root cause of mental issues. I was finding that there were so many deep-rooted issues, causing and contributing to mental health challenges that are overlooked by modern medicine. I was finally equipped with enough knowledge and determination to heal my mind and body. I can honestly say that hitting rock bottom was one of the best things that ever happened to me.

You may have had a similar experience to mine or a completely different one. Either way, we all have our own experiences that lead up to how we are feeling today. Your experience with trauma could be as simple as losing your parents at the grocery store, or It could be as complex as dealing with abuse, your sexuality, or a loved one's death. Everybody has their own story and I encourage you to scan your childhood to pinpoint any possible triggers that could have compromised your sense of security. Anxiety is a feeling of unsafety in this world, your surroundings, and even in your own mind. Exposing these childhood memories, working through them as an adult, and healing, are an essential part in overcoming anxiety.

Covid-19 Pandemic and its Effect on Mental Health

As I write this book, there is a global pandemic happening called Covid-19. It first broke out in late 2019 and has left the world shut down for most of 2020. As of late 2020, there have been over 100 million cases and 2 million deaths worldwide. Millions of people have lost their jobs, businesses have been shut down, schools have shut down, and stay-at-home orders have been put in place. Once bustling, busy metropolitan cities have turned into ghost towns. Masks must be worn when outside, constant hand washing is recommended, and maintaining a 6-foot distance from everyone around you is required. Most people can't even see their family members, because it's the elderly generation that are at most risk, so solitude has become the new norm for many people.

In addition to this horrible pandemic, we've experienced an intense re-election year, the Black Lives Matter movement, and the worst fire season the West Coast has ever seen. The intense re-election year has left the United States bitterly divided. The two parties hate each other so much and have become so preoccupied with winning, that they have left the American people angry and hopeless. As the Black Lives Matter movement has emerged, there has been a wave of peaceful, yet sometimes violent demonstrations and riots around the U.S. The movement is calling for an end to police brutality, stereotyping, and racial profiling, which has shined a negative light on law enforcement. To top this off, the West Coast has experienced the worst wildfire season in history. I live in San Francisco, and I can tell you personally that I've never experienced anything like it. If you lived in California, Oregon, or Washington, in late summer of 2020, you could not leave your house without experiencing intense smoke and drizzling dust particles, surrounded by an eerie orange tinted apocalyptic sky.

The media has had a field fest with all of these events, and in my opinion, has spiraled out of control. The media has become a super spreader of negativity, stress, fear, hate, and anger, which has caused a further divide within our country. All news is not bad news, however there is a delicate balance of educating yourself on current events, while not overwhelming yourself with nonsensical negative drama. Overconsumption of media can take a toll on your mental and physical health by increasing your stress levels and instilling fear. After being anxiety free for over 10 years, I found my anxiety slightly creeping back in. I noticed I started feeling light panicky sensations, as well as fearful negative thoughts. I knew it was a result of all the news I was watching, because just like everybody else in mid-2020, I was glued to the news because of everything happening around us.

So now, millions of people have lost their jobs and are faced with financial hardship. This stress can manifest itself into a range of physical and mental health issues. The pressure of being able to provide for yourself or your family can take a toll on the body. Chronic stress can lead to deterioration of the brain, which leaves you vulnerable to more stress, resulting in anxiety and depression.

Now consider the front-line healthcare workers and caregivers who witnessed these tragedies firsthand. Most hospitals were unprepared for the influx of Covid-19 cases. There was a substantial lack of healthcare workers, hospital space, and equipment available at the time. This left healthcare workers struggling to keep up and forced to make gut wrenching decisions on who will live and who will die. These healthcare workers were also the last people to see dying patients, as family members were not allowed to see their loved ones due to quarantine. These healthcare workers are suffering from mental and physical exhaustion, while risking their own lives on a daily basis. Being exposed to extreme morbidity and mortality can have a huge impact on one's mental health. What these healthcare workers went through can easily be compared to being at war, which leaves them susceptible to post traumatic stress disorder (PTSD).

Consider the effect that this will have on our younger generations. In the first 5 - 7 years of life, children's brains are like sponges. It's during this time of development that they are programming and building their foundation on how they will handle situations in the future. Emotional trauma experienced during this delicate time will be stored in this foundation and can reveal itself as anxiety and depression later in life. During this challenging time, it's important to maintain a child's innocence, happiness, and excitement, rather than infusing them with fear. Anxiety is based on fear, resulting from an infringement on one's safety and security, especially in early development. Let your children know that they are protected and safe, despite the challenges going on around them.

So here we are wondering what has happened to our once thought to be safe world we live in. I'm sure everyone who has lived through 2020 can say that a sense of their safety and security has been compromised. This type of trauma can have an everlasting effect, especially to those already vulnerable to mental health challenges and the younger generations. Reports have shown mental health issues, substance abuse, and suicide are on the rise and will most likely continue way into the future. Now is the time to put an emphasis on mental health, which is why I'm here to try to educate and provide you with the tools to help regain control of your life.

Flow with Your Fears

"What you resist, persists, what you look at disappears." — *Neale Donald Walsh*

I'm going to start by introducing you to a concept that really helped kickstart my recovery 10 years ago, which is simply welcoming and allowing the anxiety to flow through you without resistance.

When you feel a panic attack coming along, welcome it, feel it, observe the fearful thoughts you're experiencing, as well as the sensations going through your body. The fearful thoughts, the increased heart rate, the shallow breathing; don't fight it, just let them flow through you. Be an observer of every part of this experience; how the panic started, how it felt, and how it eventually subsided. Take every anxious episode as an opportunity to desensitize yourself toward the fear. You do this by repeatedly exposing yourself to your fears, not showing that you're scared of what you're feeling. Closely observe the situation as if you are an outsider of the whole experience.

Ok, I know you're probably thinking to yourself that if you were able to face your fears, you wouldn't be sitting here reading this book. What you may not realize is that you are in fact fully capable of facing your fears, and I will provide you with the tools necessary to support you through this. You may have to "fake it, 'til you make it," but you will get there! This process is an important initial step on the road to recovery because we need to be able to eliminate the fear associated with anxiety to focus on healing from within.

The idea behind facing your fears is that continuously facing your fears head on will eventually desensitize you toward your fear. Think of your bossy brain like a bully. A bully enjoys picking on people who they know they can get a rise out of. The more attention the person gives the bully, the more they want to keep bullying them. Once the person no longer fears the bully, the bully gets bored and moves on to someone else. It's the same idea here. The way you achieve this is through repeatedly exposing yourself to your bully and showing them you're not scared of them, until they get bored of you. It will get to the point where you're telling your bully, "I don't have time for you right now, I'm busy!" And then eventually, you'll forget that this bully even exists. You might be skeptical about this process right now, but I promise you, this method really does work!

First, we will need to get your stress response back in check so you can think clearly and focus on the rest of your recovery. If you're currently experiencing anxiety, or tend to be more anxious than most people, then you most likely have elevated levels of stress hormones running through your body. Continuously elevated stress hormones keep you in a state of panic, making it impossible to overcome anxiety. Once we get your stress levels in check, then we can focus on flowing with your fears.

Note that we are not eliminating your anxiety in this step, we are eliminating your fear of anxiety, which allows you to gain more control of your bossy brain. Once you're able to gain control, we'll work on healing, balancing, and strengthening your body so that you can put your anxiety behind you once and for all.

Ok, let's begin with understanding how stress is affecting us, how we can manage it, and how to alter our negative thoughts.

Chapter 2: Stop Stressing Out!

All of us have experienced occasional stressors in our lives and sometimes a small amount of stress can actually be a good thing for productivity. It's when acute stress turns into chronic stress that it becomes an issue. When someone experiences stress often or on a daily basis, it can lead to chronic stress. Anxious people tend to have higher stress levels, meaning that they have a continuous rush of stress hormones running through their body. It's these stress hormones that keep the vicious cycle of panic going. This is why eliminating stress should be one of the first steps in overcoming anxiety.

To put the damaging effects of stress into perspective, take a situation where someone needs an organ transplant. Our immune system is equipped to fight any foreign invaders, which includes a new organ. Before someone receives a transplant, they need to be injected with stress hormones. The reason for this is that the stress hormones suppress the immune system, so it doesn't attack the new organ. Isn't that crazy?! The surgeon deliberately causes your body stress in order to shut down your immune system. Now imagine what continuous stress is doing to your body on a daily basis. Your body will no longer be able to protect itself against colds, viruses, infection, and disease.

The stress hormone cortisol is actually an anti-inflammatory hormone that protects your nerves and tissues from damage caused by inflammation. So, at moderate levels, cortisol is actually beneficial to your body. However, chronic stress keeps your adrenal glands on overdrive by pumping out excessive amounts of cortisol. This can lead to tissue breakdown and a lowered immune system. The anti-inflammatory response becomes weakened, which means that cortisol can no longer protect your body from inflammation, thereby leading to higher inflammation throughout the body. Inflammation is known to block the neural pathways making it harder to send the signals needed in order for the brain to function properly. This blockage also interferes with the production and transportation of the happy chemicals to the brain.

Inflammation can also lead to colds and viruses, which is why people with chronic stress get sick often. An example of this is when someone who is chronically stressed takes a vacation and ironically gets sick once they are there. Well, it's actually not so ironic and there's a biological explanation behind it. Once this person is in a relaxed, stress free state, their body is no longer pumping out anti-inflammatory cortisol. We know that inflammation leads to colds and viruses, so now cortisol levels go down, and inflammation flares up. So, this whole time, the elevated levels of stress hormones were artificially keeping the body from getting sick. Now inflammation increases, and the person gets sick as a result of it.

The Stressful Amygdala

The amygdala is the part of your brain that assesses stressful situations and triggers the "fight or flight" response. Think of the amygdala as a guard dog who is ready to sound the alarm when it senses danger. This alarm releases stress hormones to increase blood pressure, heart rate, breathing, and muscle tension; all necessary in order to provide you with the energy needed to overcome a threat.

People with anxiety most likely have an overactive amygdala, which could result in an underactive hippocampus. The hippocampus is the portion of the brain responsible for memory, fear inhibition,

21

and stress control, so it essentially keeps the amygdala in check. Chronic stress can eventually deteriorate the hippocampus, which means that the loss of this portion of the brain weakens your ability to control stress. That said, chronic stress can literally change the size, structure, and function of your brain. This would leave the person vulnerable to more stress, more anxiety, depression, and other cognitive issues.

Ok, now that I've caused you more stress, let's see how we can reverse this damage. Luckily, the brain has neuroplasticity, meaning the brain is adaptable and able to create new neural pathways, reversing any damage caused by chronic stress. The damage can be reversed through physical exercise, brain exercise, diet, and meditation, which have all been shown to decrease stress, while increasing the size of your hippocampus.

1. **Exercise** is not only good for the body, but it's good for the brain too. Consider a study done on two groups of mice, one group with a hamster wheel, and another group with no hamster wheel. Those with the hamster wheel showed a larger hippocampus than those without the hamster wheel. So, the hamsters who weren't getting exercise showed smaller brains than those who were.

   Another example relates to people who develop Alzheimer's in their old age. Deterioration of the hippocampus is commonly associated with Alzheimer's, and studies have shown that a large portion of those with the disease, didn't prioritize exercise throughout their lives.

2. **Mental exercises** are another way to increase the size of your brain. Prioritizing continuous learning and problem solving is a great way to create new neural pathways. Try to learn a new language, solve jigsaw puzzles, pick up a new hobby, or play card games. You can simply even try to use your less dominant hand, which can be very stimulating for the brain. So, if you're right-handed, try using your left hand to write, pick things up, brush your teeth, or whatever else you can think of.

3. **Maintain a healthy diet** by eliminating processed junk food, while increasing your intake of healthy omega 3 fatty acids, such as salmon and nuts. Omega 3 fatty acids are anti-inflammatory and contain antioxidants, which can help regenerate the brain. Remember that inflammation in the brain causes it to shrink and age prematurely, so we need to avoid foods that promote inflammation, while consuming those that fight it.

4. **Meditation** has been shown to thicken the brain, as well as alter its physical structure. The thickening is shown to occur in the portion responsible for cognition, emotional processing, and general well-being. Meditation enlarges the prefrontal cortex, which is the rational decision-making part of the brain. It also shrinks the "stressful" amygdala, while thickening the "calming" hippocampus. It can also increase grey matter, which is linked to intelligence.

Insight Meditation

This is a great type of meditation to help you learn how to keep your cool and let things go! Insight Meditation, also known as Vipassana, is the basis of all Buddhist meditations. It's a type of meditation that helps calm your thoughts by diverting your attention to sensory experiences, such as your breathing, rather than what's going on in your mind. This type of meditation can be used as a way to get in control of your physiological response triggered by anxious thoughts. It can also be a good type of meditation for beginners to try.

You can start out by getting in a comfortable seated position or lying down. Close your eyes and begin to take slow deep breaths. Take as many breaths as you need in order to get into a relaxed state. You should continue breathing at a normal pace, while focusing your attention on your abdominal breathing. Pay attention to how your abdomen rises when you take a deep breath and falls when you exhale. You can assist yourself in keeping your attention focused by saying the word "rising" as you take a deep breath, and "falling" while you exhale.

The goal here is to keep focusing on your abdominal breathing. If you sense something around you, acknowledge it, but try your best not to put any thought into it. Let your thoughts dissipate, while just being an observer of the present moment. If you hear a noise around you, just be a listener. Don't try to understand it or think about it. If you feel a sensation in your body such as an itch or tickle, just acknowledge it and let it be. You can acknowledge the distraction by naming it. For example, if you feel an itch, think of the word "itch," rather than thinking about how or why it's itching. If someone honks their horn, think of the word "horn," rather than wonder why the person is honking. With each distracting thought, you should redivert yourself to your abdominal breathing.

By doing this meditation for 15 - 30 minutes a day, 3 days a week, you can start to see improvements in clarity, focus, and stress reduction, which are all connected to your hippocampus. Strengthening your hippocampus can help you regulate your emotional well-being, which is usually what is destroyed by an overactive fearful amygdala. Insight meditation can help eliminate random useless thinking by emphasizing the present moment instead.

Busy Brain - Digital Detox

Modern day living has become busier than ever with bustling cities, busy work schedules, emails, meetings, social engagements, social media, nonsensical news, and political drama. This sensory overload keeps the brain on such high alert that the body literally starts to look at information as an actual threat. The busy brain becomes so preoccupied and addicted to information that it becomes fearful of missing out, better known as FOMO. Now the emotional part of the brain called the amygdala triggers the "fight or flight" response to deal with the perceived threat. This means that the amygdala has set off its guard dogs to pump out excessive stress hormones.

The problem with a busy brain is that it interferes with our ability to unwind, sleep, focus, remember things, and pay attention. It's hard for the person to even realize that they are suffering from a busy brain because they are so caught up in this sensory overload. When in a busy brain state, there's not a lot of cognition available for use, so the brain relies on sensory memory. The brain no longer has an attention span to learn new things or focus on the present moment. Busy brain interferes with a person's ability to take in new information. They also find it challenging to observe and assess their surroundings because they are so preoccupied in their thoughts. This diminishes the person's ability to multitask, catch mistakes, and react quickly. For example, someone with a busy brain has a higher likelihood of getting into a car accident. Driving usually involves running on autopilot, but the person must be able to observe and assess their surroundings. Someone experiencing a busy brain could miss a red light, stop sign, or misjudge other drivers' actions, which puts them at a higher risk of getting into an accident.

Do you find yourself excessively checking your social media account or emails? Do you find yourself overwhelmed or stressed out with work, emails, and meetings, but you find yourself still distracted by social media, which only seems to add more stress in your life? Do you find yourself easily distracted and forgetful of what you were doing prior to the distraction? Do you have a poor memory or find it hard to focus and stay focused? If so, then you may be suffering from a busy brain, and those with anxiety are more prone to it than the average person.

Ways to cure a busy brain

1. **Make a list** to organize and prioritize your thoughts or goals. Tackle each task one at a time and avoid multitasking. After each task is accomplished, cross it off your list.

2. **Declutter your living space or workspace**. Do a purge and get rid of the clutter in your life, which will help you get rid of the excess clutter in your brain. Go for simplicity, lots of white and bright light in your space.

3. **Do yoga, breathing exercises or meditate** in order to encourage the relaxation response. These can also bring you back to the present moment, which is essential to a relaxed mind.

4. **Listen to a podcast or read a book**. Try to distract your mind from going in different directions by focusing all your attention on one thing. Make sure the topic is lighthearted and not challenging in order to avoid any stress.

5. **Avoid electronics**, such as cell phones, iPads, laptops, computers, TVs, and any other devices. Only have one electronic open at a time, and only a few browsers on your computer to encourage simplicity and avoid distraction. Avoid checking social media and personal emails throughout the day.

6. **Make a list of all the things that may be distracting you on a daily basis**. When you find yourself distracted by these things, make a conscious effort not to pay attention to them as much as possible. For example, social media is an addiction, which means that a person will need to re-learn how to live without it before it becomes natural again. You may experience withdrawals, but the more you abstain from checking your social media account, the easier it will get. This isn't to say that you should abstain completely. The goal would be to significantly reduce engagement time, so that you're not negatively affected by it anymore.

Dopamine fasting or a dopamine diet can be done to rebalance the brain's motivation-reward system. The fast involves abstaining from all activities that involve pleasure, including food, alcohol, sex, masturbation, social media, video games, TV, and talking. The fast can be done for one day on a monthly basis. The only things you should allow yourself to do is drink water, be in nature, do some light exercise, meditate, and write in a journal. The point is to cut out all over stimulating activities so that your brain stops excessively pumping out dopamine, especially with negative behaviors. We'll learn more about dopamine in The Happy Chemicals chapter of this book.

Coffee - The Adrenaline Junkie

Caffeine is known to stimulate the central nervous system, as well as increase dopamine production, which is the reason you feel more alert after consuming a cup of coffee. It inhibits adenosine, which is a neurotransmitter that promotes sleepiness, while increasing the stress hormone, cortisol. It also increases serotonin, which is why caffeine can actually be a mood booster. In moderate amounts, it can actually boost brain function, improve focus, and even possibly reduce your risk of degenerative diseases, such as Alzheimer's or dementia.

The problem is that someone with anxiety most likely already has an overactive nervous system, leaving them in a constant hypersensitive state. Having a cup of coffee will intensify this hyperactivity, leading to higher levels of stressful cortisol in their body. So, the positive effects of drinking a cup of coffee turn negative when done in excess or if the person has anxiety. It can overstimulate your brain and central nervous system, resulting in a lack of focus, mental confusion, nervousness, jitteriness, and hypersensitivity. When someone with anxiety has one cup of coffee, it's as if it's their third cup of the day because they already have excessive stress hormones running through their body. Adding a cup of coffee will just increase these stress levels even more.

At 27 years old I experienced the worst panic attack of my life. The attack was a result of binge drinking the night before, a strong cup of coffee, 2 hours of sleep, and an early morning cigarette. It was a recipe for disaster. This panic attack left me in a hazy, fearful brain fog for weeks. Throughout those weeks I would consistently have little aftershocks of panic, caused by my elevated stress levels. Every panic attack afterward would keep this vicious cycle going by adding more stress hormones to my body. My nervous system was beat up and on complete overdrive. When I would finally rest at night, my body would vibrate for 10 seconds every few minutes as I fell asleep. I would literally feel my nervous system disarming itself as my body would vibrate in 2-minute intervals as I began to relax. Yes, I said vibrate. It was the weirdest sensation, but I didn't mind it because I could tell that my body was entering a relaxed state.

During the following weeks my stress levels were off the charts. My adrenal glands were on overdrive, constantly pumping adrenaline throughout my body. Eventually, after quitting smoking, cutting out coffee, incorporating meditation, yoga, and lots of sleep, the hazy panicky feeling began to subside. I thought I was in the clear, so I slowly started to drink coffee again. A few days later I noticed that I was getting a constant dull pain above my kidneys. I couldn't figure out why this pain was happening, so I began to do some research. I found that the adrenal glands are located in that exact area. Adrenal glands help regulate the way our body responds to stress, so of course my glands were shot. There's something called adrenal fatigue, which can be aggravated by coffee. So, I decided to give up coffee to see if it went away and sure enough it did! I couldn't believe that a single cup of coffee each day was causing me to suffer from adrenal fatigue.

This made me really think about how a morning cup of coffee affects our body. Every time you drink a cup of coffee, stress hormones are released. Combine that with chronic stress or anxiety, and you end up with exhausted adrenal glands. So, if you're someone who has anxiety but loves your morning cup of coffee, I would suggest taking a good look at whether coffee could be provoking your symptoms. You might be freaking out right now telling yourself you can't survive without coffee, but I promise you will!

Oxidative Stress

Oxidative stress is an imbalance between free radicals and antioxidants in your body. Free radicals are actually beneficial to your body at low levels because they help fight off certain pathogens. Antioxidants keep free radicals in check, because at high levels, free radicals can harm the central nervous system. Oxidative stress can affect your body in the same way that regular stress can, which can contribute to anxiety. This is why it's important to limit your exposure to toxins, such as smoking cigarettes, drinking alcohol, drugs, pollution, pesticides, radiation, and overconsumption of sugars, fats, and processed foods.

To put oxidative stress into perspective, consider the hangover you experience the next day after drinking. Alcohol causes high levels of oxidative stress in the body which contributes to that anxious hangover feeling you get the next day. When you drink a freshly squeezed fruit or veggie juice after a night of drinking, it helps fight off the free radicals that are overwhelming your body, which lessens the hangover and anxiety.

The key in overcoming anxiety is limiting the amount of stress in the body, which includes oxidative stress. So, if you think you may be suffering from oxidative stress, I'd recommend that you incorporate lots of fruits and veggies in your diet to offset this imbalance.

Chapter 2: In a Nutshell

1. The portion of the brain responsible for the "flight or fight" response is the amygdala. Think of this portion of the brain as your guard dog. It's important to learn how to tame this dog because every time he barks, your body pumps out more stress hormones. A continuous amount of stress hormones running through your body makes it easier to trigger another panic attack. Try to rid yourself of these extra stress hormones to level the playing field against your bossy brain.

2. Stop stressing out! Chronic stress can make it harder for your body to control stress in the future. It can also lead to inflammation, which blocks the neural pathways, as well as the production and transportation of the happy chemicals.

3. Stress can literally shrink your brain. Luckily, this can be reversed through stress reduction, physical exercise, brain exercise, a healthy diet, and meditation.

4. Every time you drink a cup of coffee, your adrenal glands pump out stress hormones. Someone with anxiety most likely has an excess amount of stress hormones running through their body.

Adding a cup of coffee can lead to more anxiety and adrenal fatigue.

5. Did you know that eating fruits and veggies could actually fight stress? Oxidative stress is another type of stress that comes in the form of free radicals. Your body uses up antioxidants to fight these free radicals, so you need to make sure to limit your exposure to toxins, while increasing your intake of fruits and veggies.

Chapter 3: Good Vibes Only

"Just because you are happy, it does not mean that the day is perfect, but that you have looked beyond its imperfections." - Bob Marley

The bossy brain loves drama, fear, and negativity because that's what it feeds off to stay alive. Think back to our caveman roots. Our brains were programmed to react strongly to negative stimuli in order to protect us against danger. But in this day and age, we no longer need to fear being prey as we once did before.

Anxious people tend to think more negatively than non-anxious people do, and this is usually mentally programmed from early childhood. They usually worry about future events or situations and view these scenarios as an unpredictable threat. They usually spend a lot of time worrying about the worst-case scenario, especially those that are out of their control. All this time spent worrying about something that may or may not happen, is robbing them of being in the present moment. A lot of time is spent overestimating the likelihood of something bad happening, while underestimating their power over the situation. This causes them to over plan for all possible scenarios. Once the scenario has successfully passed, the anxious person doesn't lower their negative outlook on the situation as a non-anxious person would. They usually think that they got lucky and that their fear could certainly occur in the future with the same probability.

My mother has suffered from anxiety for a majority of her life. She has a fear of deadly diseases, a fear of having someone driving her around, and a fear of elevators. She also always over plans for the worst possible outcomes of every situation. Watching her exhibit these fears as a child really affected me. Being fearful of everything became first nature and I thought it was perfectly normal to live this way. It was weird to me when I saw people not overly cautious like I was. Eventually, this fearful attitude spiraled into panic attacks and hypochondria.

My case of hypochondria began when I was around 9 years old. I remember my mom had this book of symptoms and disease. I became obsessed, constantly cross referencing my "symptoms" with this book. This became a daily ritual, and the worst part was that I was hiding it from everyone, which was intensifying the problem. I remember thinking my stretch marks were a dangerous disease because I learned in our health class that red streaks were a sign of a spreading infection. I would hide them from everyone and constantly check if they were still there throughout the day. I also thought the purple veins in my wrist were cancer. I remember having a bladder infection at 16 years old and thinking it was kidney disease. It didn't matter that my symptoms were more likely connected to a bladder infection. My brain would default to believing the worst-case scenario because this is how it was programmed since early childhood.

Someone with hypochondria needs to make sure that they get their stress levels in check. The stress from worrying alone can cause all kinds of physical symptoms that can be mistaken for disease. You can learn to relax through yoga, meditation, exercise, listening to soothing music, and getting enough sleep. Having a relaxed mind and body will take away any physical symptoms associated with stress.

Ok, so we're all guilty of symptom checking on the internet, right? Sometimes the internet can be great at providing information. But if you find that it's feeding into your hypochondria, then it's time to take a break. Your bossy brain feeds off of negativity, so of course it's going to be drawn to the worst possible scenario. Rather than obsessing over what could or couldn't be, go to the doctors to get a full exam. Staying on top of your health will help alleviate the worry associated with disease.

It wasn't until I was 27 years old that I forced myself to go to the doctors to get a full physical. My normal results set my mind at ease and encouraged me to live a healthier life. My bossy brain's negative narrative took me to a really dark place in my younger years and I refuse to let it take away any more of my headspace.

Being that we're predisposed to negative thinking, we need to reprogram our brains to think more positive. You can start by acknowledging a negative thought when it comes through. As you become aware of your negative thoughts, they will automatically begin to shift. I'm telling you; this really does work! Most of the day our brain is running on autopilot, and if your brain is used to negative thinking, then this is what it's going to default to. Also, it's impossible to reprogram your brain when it's running on autopilot. In order for reprogramming to occur, you need to be present and aware of your thoughts. Once you start catching yourself in your negativity, you can shift these thoughts to more neutral or positive ones. Try listening to your thoughts from an outside perspective and see if there's a more optimistic way to interpret the situation. You can also do this by writing in a journal. Every time you notice that you're writing about something negative, scratch it out and replace it with something more neutral or positive.

The media thrives off of negativity, so make a conscious effort to filter out any unnecessary news you're listening to. The same thing goes for that amazing new drama series that everyone is talking about. Replace the drama for something lighthearted or educational. Who you surround yourself with also plays a big role in your thought process, so try to limit your time spent with those who tend to be more negative.

Learn to be present with each circumstance that you find yourself in and try not to create a story in your mind. If you find that you're stuck in a traffic jam, then just let it be. Don't honk your horn, get mad, or swerve through traffic; just be at peace with it. If you're holding a grudge toward someone in your life, forgive them and let it go. You need to be able to forgive in order to be in the present moment, otherwise you're living in the past. Think of a time that you got in a fight with someone and held onto the anger toward them. You go about your daily life only to hear their name come up at some point in the future. Notice the stress, anger, and negativity this feeling brings upon you. You're holding on to this anger and storing it in your subconscious only for it to come out at a later time. This animosity is stored in your body as negative energy. You may think that you've moved on, but if you haven't forgiven the person, then you're still stuck with this negative energy. "Resentment is like drinking poison and waiting for the other person to die." Really try to think about this quote. Animosity is toxic for your body, and it reveals itself through stress and negativity. The only person you're hurting by holding onto resentment is yourself.

It's important to set aside your ego and work through your problems. If you're dealing with someone who is difficult, then you may be better off telling them that you understand where they are coming from and make peace with them. This doesn't mean that you're accepting that they are right, and you are wrong. It just means that you are choosing peace over ego, and you refuse to carry this burden around with you. Think about what will happen if you walk away from that friend with the issue unresolved. You'll continue to imagine the argument later, stressing yourself further by storytelling in your mind. How unfair your friend was being, what else you could have said, how you're right, and they're wrong. Let it go! Surrender to the situation. Forgive, forget, agree to disagree. You need to learn to surrender to your current circumstance and let things be as they are. Don't continue to stress about the situation, wondering how things could have been different. Just accept that it is what it is and live in the present moment.

Be present and aware of your thoughts and emotions. Retrain your brain to acknowledge and let go of negative emotions as they arise. Do not story-tell in your mind. Do not ask yourself any could have, should have, or would haves. It is what it is! Don't try to actively control or resist your negative emotions. Just "be an observer of the mind" as Eckhart Tolle would say. Being the observer of your mind helps you become more thought conscious and brings you to the present moment. Be conscious of your thoughts, but don't overthink them. Simply acknowledging negative thoughts as they come in is enough to retrain your brain.

Maintaining this outlook will help you attract more of what you want in life and less of what you don't want. Learn how to turn obstacles into opportunities by finding the positive uniqueness in every situation. Also, ask yourself if there's anything you can learn from the situation. Saying you're unlucky, life isn't fair, you've been dealt a bad hand, or any other negative outlook only brings you more negativity in your life. Learn how to turn struggles into success, obstacles into opportunities, and use each challenging situation as an opportunity for self-growth.

Poker Face

Ok, so now we're all peaceful and Zen, only to get hit with another panic attack, causing our stress levels to go up again. Anyone who's had one knows that feeling of wanting to jump out of your skin to escape the world. But the reality is you're stuck in this body being bossed around by your brain. Your heart's throbbing, about to pop out of your chest, that lifesaving breath you can't take, the dizziness, the hot flashes, the lightheadedness, and don't even get me started on that feeling of unreality.

Panic attacks can be provoked or unprovoked, but for the most part, they seem to come out of nowhere. The truth of the matter is, it's your bossy brain taking a scary thought and blowing it way out of proportion. Now, it triggered your "fight or flight" response, and you have excessive stress hormones rushing through your body as if you have a lion chasing you. This is why your vitals are going wild, giving you a sense of unreality. Your body is packed with adrenaline and ready to jet, except there's nowhere to run to. If you sprint for 20 minutes next time you get a full-blown panic attack, I bet you'd be able to run faster than someone in the Olympics.

Now you got to get your relaxation response to kick in so your body can stop pumping those stress hormones. Someone who has continuous panic attacks has a constant over supply of stress hormones running through their body. This is why it's so easy for your bossy brain to trigger the response again at the drop of a dime. The key is to kick on your relaxation response long enough to get rid of all the excessive stress hormones. You can get your body to relax within a few minutes by doing some deep breathing exercises. Once you're in a relaxed state, adrenaline will stop pumping, and it will leave your system within 20 - 40 minutes. Try your best to remain relaxed so that the adrenaline can leave your body as soon as possible. If you feel another panic attack come along, follow the same process by trying to get yourself to relax.

The liver is responsible for breaking down and processing hormones. This means that your liver needs to be in good shape in order to efficiently eliminate stress hormones. Those with chronic stress and anxiety most likely have an abundance of stress hormones running through their body. This is because their liver has been on overdrive and can't process all these hormones at once. Not only does this contribute to more anxiety, but it inhibits the production of melatonin which is essential to a good night's sleep. Those with anxiety may benefit from a liver detox to help this organ function optimally.

So, once the adrenaline leaves your body, you'll have more control over your bossy brain. You'll be in a better position to tell it to "back off" next time it tries to take a fearful thought to the next level. Get sassy with your brain because there's actually some real power behind talking to yourself this way. I got to the point where I'd make fun of my brain for creating these fearful thoughts. I would sometimes even act out my fears. I would roll my eyes and dwindle down to the floor as if I passed out. Then I'd bust out laughing and ask myself, "What happened? Why are we still awake? I thought we were passing out?"

Here's how you can get sassy with your bossy brain next time panic comes over you. Say ...

- Let's do this! I'm ready! Bring it on!
- Is that all you got? I'm ready for more!
- Back off, I'm busy right now! No one cares!
- If you think we're going crazy, let's go crazy!
- Whatever! I don't care! Get over it!
- You think we're going to pass out, so let's pass out!
- Nobody's got time for this!

Don't look at this self-talk as if you're diminishing your self-worth, you're simply turning something scary into something lighthearted. You're calling your bossy brain's bluff. Imagine that you're in a poker game and you're going head-to-head with your bossy brain. Once you start gaining more control, you can start turning each panic attack into an opportunity to reprogram your brain. The more you call its bluff, the bigger your pot will grow, and your fear of panic attacks will slowly start to diminish. This is exactly what you want, because any new panic attacks will pump more stress hormones back in your body, which is what keeps the perpetual cycle going.

Don't get down on yourself if you find that you're making progress and have a panic attack that sets you back a bit. You will have setbacks, this is a part of the process, but the more you do this, the stronger you'll get.

You can also trick your bossy brain through distractions, like cleaning the house, making a phone call, going for a quick run, or dancing around like a goofball. Sometimes when I'd feel a panic attack coming along, I'd grab my guitar, which I have no idea how to play, turn up the music really loud, jump on my bed, and rock it out as if I were a rock star in the 80's. Before I knew it, my anxiety shifted from fear to fun in the matter of minutes. Wiggle your body, do the twist, shake your booty, do the arm wave, just be goofy and flow with the nervousness. You could even just simply continue doing what you were doing before the thoughts of panic came over you, not giving your bossy brain any attention. Only now, put extra focus on what you were doing as if it's the most interesting thing in the world. If you maintain the distraction long enough, the panicky feeling will go away, and you'll forget that it even started to creep up on you.

The key is to neutralize your nervousness by flowing with it, rather than against it. Think of the saying "go with the flow." Flow with the current, not against it. Think of how much energy you'd be wasting going against the current in a choppy ocean. Now think of how much easier it would be to just float and flow with the waves, saving your energy for when the waves calm down. It's the same concept here. Stop fighting your anxious thoughts, just flow with them. Be present with your thoughts because this is how you'll expose them for what they truly are, just thoughts. Your thoughts are not you; they are just thoughts. An anxious thought is just your bossy brain's creative imagination going wild.

So, when you feel the next panic attack coming along, don't show your cards. Call your bossy brain's bluff. Again, turn the attack into an opportunity to retrain your brain. You can also take this opportunity to get cheesy and do some positive self-talk to boost your confidence.

Use conviction in your words and tell yourself …

- I am a badass!
- I am unstoppable!
- I am fearless!
- I am strong!
- I am courageous!
- I am confident!
- I am capable of overcoming anything!

You really want to believe these things that you're telling yourself. Don't just say the words. Let them penetrate your body, through your heart, down to your bones. Feel it to be true so that eventually you will embody the fierceness and unstoppable badass that you really are!

Anxious thoughts trigger your "fight or flight" response, which is what gives you all those scary sensations. So, take it for what it is, it's your body's stress response, and that's it! It's there to protect you from a perceived threat, except there's no actual threat in front of you. Now those stress hormones are running rampant throughout your body, causing you to feel like you're losing your mind. Your goal now is to turn on your relaxation response long enough to get rid of those extra stress hormones. If you find that your breathing is shallow, try to do some abdominal breathing to supply your brain with plenty of oxygen. This will help calm you down and bring your heart rate back to normal.

Ok, I've suffered from panic attacks for almost 18 years, so I know that each panic attack feels just as scary as the first one. I get how easy it is to throw rational thoughts out the window. Or how it feels impossible to tell yourself that you've experienced this feeling before. You're probably convinced that this will be the time that your worst fears will come true.

What you may not realize is that it's during these panic attacks where mental reprogramming occurs. This is what makes it the most effective time to recondition your brain. This process of self-talk is an example of interoceptive therapy, which we'll learn about later in this book. The process involves welcoming a panic attack so that you can sit through it while keeping your cool until the feeling goes away. Sometimes when I felt a panic attack coming along, I would sit in a computer chair, spinning in circles until I felt dizzy. Once I stopped, I would let myself feel the sensations going through my body. I would wait it out no matter how uncomfortable it was. Ok, I know this sounds counter-intuitive, like "why would I bring on a panic attack when it's the exact thing I'm trying to avoid?" But this is the point. You need to get comfortable with being uncomfortable. Avoiding your fear only makes it stronger, while facing your fear weakens it. If you're no longer fearing the attack, then it loses strength because you're no longer focusing on it. Think of your bossy brain like a bully.

The more you feed into the bully, the more they want to keep bullying you. You become boring to the bully when you stop paying attention to them, so they go off to bully someone else. So, don't feed into the bully.

By using this technique, I was able to desensitize myself enough to get control of my bossy brain. I was able to eliminate random panic attacks completely. The only time I would experience an attack is when I provoked it by exposing myself to a known trigger, such as coffee or some other stimulant. I haven't had an unprovoked attack for over 10 years, and I can't even give myself one if I tried. It's a liberating feeling, and anyone is capable of achieving this.

Figuring out what works for you will most likely be trial and error. Some of my suggestions above may make you feel worse, while some might make you feel better. It's during these episodes that you should try different techniques to figure out what works for you. Welcome the panic with open arms and take the opportunity to balance your bossy brain. Think of it like tug-a-war. Each time you're able to avoid an attack, take a little more of that rope.

Rationalizing with the Irrational Mind

Sometimes your bossy brain might try to convince you that you're going nuts, but I promise you, you're not! One day I was riding the train to work with my cousin who majored in psychology. I told her that I was suffering from repeated panic attacks and a constant sense of unreality. I told her that I literally felt like I was going insane. She giggled and told me, "Taleen, if you were actually going insane, you wouldn't know it. People who have lost touch with reality, usually aren't aware they have lost touch." Whoa … this got me thinking. Is this really true?

That afternoon I sat on the steps at the corner of Market and Montgomery Street. San Francisco has a large homeless population in which some of them suffer from untreated schizophrenia. So, I decided to sit and observe the actions of some of these people. I watched as they talked to themselves, yelled cuss words in the air, laughed hysterically out of nowhere, and played imaginary instruments. Could it be that these people were completely detached from reality? Someone with schizophrenia might experience voices in their head, see visuals of imaginary objects and people, or feel somatic symptoms, such as imaginary bugs under their skin. They can also experience delusions, such as paranoia, convinced they're being followed, targeted, tricked, or that they've been possessed by demons. I came to realize that the reason some of these people were homeless was because they were unaware of their detachment from reality. It could be that they don't have family to help them realize they have a problem. Or maybe they've refused help because they don't believe they have a problem.

Consider someone that suffers from bipolar who experiences a manic episode. They usually don't know when they're experiencing a relapse. They can feel a rush of energy, striking and sometimes destructive ideas, intense thoughts of creativity, or even experience delusional behavior, such as visual hallucinations or extreme paranoia. At that moment, they're convinced that what they are feeling is in fact reality. It's not uncommon for someone who experiences mania to regret the things they did during a manic episode. Family, friends, or colleagues are usually the first people to notice that there is a problem. When confronted by the people around them, they usually refuse treatment, believing that they are perfectly normal. They may even become paranoid that those around them are trying to hurt them.

I'll never forget what my cousin told me that day and I've used it to rationalize my fear of insanity many times. People with anxiety rarely experience delusions or hallucinations, and the fact that they are concerned with going insane is a clear indication that they are not. Also, anxious people are usually hyper-aware of their actions, body sensations, and surroundings, meaning that they are more likely focused on reality, rather than the detachment from it.

Chapter 3: In a Nutshell

1. The bossy brain feeds and thrives off of negativity. Unfortunately, our brains have been programmed to always think the worst-case

scenario, which goes back to our caveman roots. Luckily, we can reprogram our brains to think more positive by simply just acknowledging when a negative thought appears. It's as simple as that. Catching yourself when thinking negative thoughts will eventually automatically change your brain to think more positive.

2. Try to shift negative thoughts to positive thoughts by seeing the circumstance from a different perspective.

3. Surrender to every circumstance you find yourself in and learn how to let stuff go!

4. Avoid nonsensical media, as well as negative TV shows, movies, and people.

5. Think of your bossy brain like a bully. Don't feed into its bullying tactics. Put on your poker face and call your bossy brain's bluff. Each time you face the panic head on, you take a little bit more of that rope, so get sassy with your brain.

6. Panic attacks come with that "lovely" feeling of unreality. Know that you are not going crazy and it's the stress hormones causing you to feel that way.

Chapter 4: Face Your Fears

Expose Yourself

Exposure therapy is a psychological treatment that involves gradual and repeated exposure to a person's feared scenario or traumatic experience. It helps people face their fears rather than avoid them, because avoiding your fears only intensify them. Every time we avoid a threat and survive, it trains our brain to continue seeing our fear as a threat. When we face our fears and survive, it retrains our brain to no longer see our fear as a threat. This is why facing your fears is the best time to retrain your brain.

Exposure therapy retrains your brain to stop sending fear signals when there is no actual danger. These fear signals trigger the "fight or flight" response, enabling us to react rapidly and powerfully. This was really beneficial back in the day when humans had to worry about predators, but today this response is mostly triggered by stress and anxiety.

OCD - The Monster Inside Me

Sometimes OCD can become so intense, it's as if the bossy brain went on an Adderall binge, and didn't even give you a heads up.

OCD can come and go in waves throughout someone's life, but when it's highly active, the bossy brain morphs into a controlling monster.

My brother has suffered from OCD for most of his life. At one point, he developed Harm OCD, which involves obsessive thoughts of harming yourself or others. It's like a lost sense of control, where you feel like you don't trust yourself around others or even around yourself. My brother's intrusive thoughts involved fears of killing himself, his family, random people, hurting someone in a car accident, and other harmful thoughts. He wouldn't allow himself to drive, be around sharp objects, or even around people. The truth of the matter is my brother couldn't even hurt a fly. He was so disturbed by these intrusive thoughts that he started to question his own morals. These obsessive thoughts took over his life, leaving him unable to work, eat, sleep, or even function. The more he fought his thoughts, the worse they would get. Fighting the thoughts was fueling the bossy brain until it grew into an uncontrollable monster.

After months of suffering from Harm OCD, we finally convinced him to get help. He spent months working with therapists doing traditional forms of therapy that weren't working for him. Finally, they sent him to a clinic that specializes in OCD where he was able to overcome it within a few days. Can you believe it?! It only took a few days to overcome his Harm OCD after suffering for months.

The type of treatment they used was exposure therapy. The idea was that his resistance to the intrusive thoughts were actually making them stronger. The fact that he was avoiding driving, sharp objects, and police, was actually fueling the monster inside him. They encouraged him to face his fears by using visualization techniques or physically putting himself in his feared circumstance. For example, they had him visit a police station, since he was convinced that he belonged in jail. Being at the police station and seeing that the police paid no attention to him, made him doubt the thoughts he was having. They encouraged him to play violent video games in order to desensitize him toward his thoughts of hurting someone. Since he was avoiding sharp objects, they would have him repeatedly hold a knife for a few minutes at a time. Each time he gained more and more trust that he was not going to do anything with that knife. His thoughts are just thoughts, it's not who he really is. It's the bossy brain! As crazy as this may seem, it worked! It really worked! And it worked fast! He suffered with Harm OCD for months and was finally free within a few days after exposure therapy.

Now consider someone who has a fear of germs. They avoid touching door handles and if they do, they need to wash their hands immediately afterward. In exposure therapy, they would have them touch a door handle, but would encourage them not to wash their hands afterward. The more they abstain from acting out their compulsions, the more they will become desensitized toward their fear, which will eventually weaken their obsession. Once the obsession is no longer intrusive, it relinquishes control, because the person is no longer feeding into the obsession.

Ok, now that I've raved on about how great exposure therapy can be, let's explore the concept a bit more to see how we can apply it. Some types of exposure therapies consist of imaginal, in vivo, and interoceptive exposure. Virtual reality exposure therapy has recently emerged as a valuable tool in assisting with these types of therapies. You can find a clinic that offers it as a service or you can DIY at home, which is usually my preference.

Imaginal Exposure involves imagining, writing, and reading the person's most feared scenario, darkest thoughts, or traumatic memory. The person must imagine the traumatic scenario and narrate it out loud using present tense language. The narrative should include every detail about the scenario, such as sights, sounds, smells, surroundings, thoughts, and emotions. This process of engagement, revisiting or visiting, and processing is repeated over and over again in order to weaken the fear.

If you'd like to try this method, here are some tips in order to have the most success.

Imaginal Exposure Written Story Guidelines:

1. Use present tense language as if the scenario is happening right now.

2. Use first person language, rather than writing about someone else committing the act. Make sure the exercise is about you in the scenario.

3. Write out the whole scenario start to finish no matter how disturbing the thoughts are. There should be no shame in this exercise. It should consist of your worst fears but must remain realistic at the same time. It needs to feel believable to you.

4. List all the emotions felt, your surroundings, sounds, smells, tastes, and sight.

5. Include the repercussions or punishment as a result of the act if there is one.

The idea is to repetitively read and listen to the story to diminish the fear connected to the scenario. Therefore, the story should be reread over and over, or recorded and then listen to several times a day. Each repetition should include feelings and emotions, not just done as an exercise to get done with. Keep repeating until the story doesn't faze you anymore and actually bores you. This is a good sign, and you might be feeling some relief at this point. If you still don't feel relief, you can try the whole exercise again with a different scenario or consider having a therapist help you with the process. The therapist will know the right questions to ask, so that they can guide you through it.

In Vivo Exposure involves facing your fear in real world scenarios, rather than your imagination. For example, someone with PTSD may have a fear of objects, people, or places. Avoidance is common in PTSD and it's a defense mechanism used to prevent the traumatic experience from occurring again. In vivo exposure would have the person expose themselves to these feared situations in real life. This type of exposure therapy also works well with phobias, such as arachnophobia, which is a fear of spiders. They would be asked to look at images of tarantulas and then eventually touch one. Or consider a person with acrophobia, also known as a fear of heights. They would first start with smaller heights and eventually work their way up. The idea is to confront your feared situations, thoughts, and emotions in order to diminish the actual fear. Breathing techniques are used to help calm yourself down during the exposure.

I recently developed a fear of heights a few years ago. I can't tell you what triggered this fear, but it revealed itself when I took a ferris wheel ride with my ex-boyfriend and some friends. I had an intense fear that I would somehow fall out of the ferris wheel while in mid-air. I was panicking so hard that I had to sit on the floor with my eyes closed until the ride was over.

The next time it occurred was when I was in Phoenix, Arizona, hiking Camelback Mountain. The mountain has an elevation of 2,700 feet and gorgeous panoramic views of the city once you reach the top. Well, once I hit the top, I had this gut-wrenching fear that I was going to accidentally fall off the mountain. I had to drop to the floor, lay down, and close my eyes to calm myself down. Suddenly a new fear of rolling off the mountain came over me. My friends tried to encourage me to calm down to enjoy the scenery, but I was insistent on rushing my way down the mountain.

During the same trip, I had made my way to Sedona which was one of my bucket list destinations for quite some time. I was climbing up Cathedral Rock which has a hiking elevation of 645 feet. This may not seem high, but it turns very steep, very quick! While going up, I'm feeling great because I'm not taking the time to look at what's below me. It wasn't until I stopped at this small ledge to gaze at the impeccably breathtaking landscape that I felt the same terror creep its way back in. "Holy crap, it's happening again!" And now I was on this small ledge perched 300 feet in the air and had to make my way down. I decided enough is enough. I wasn't going to let my fear of heights rob me from this experience.

I was going to put an end to my fear by making my way back down the mountain and then gradually acclimating myself to the increasing elevations. So, I hiked my way back to the bottom to start all over again. I would stop every 10 feet or so to sit back and take in the beautiful view. If the uncomfortable feeling came upon me, I would sit with it and take deep breaths throughout the moment. If it felt too overwhelming, I would work my way back down to the prior stopping point until I felt comfortable again. Then I would work my way back up to try it again. I was eventually able to work my way back up to 300 feet and sit there for about an hour or so with minimal discomfort.

Desensitizing your anxiety through in vivo exposure will most likely take some time and will be very gradual. Everyone's comfort level is different, and the exposure should be done at a slightly uncomfortable pace.

Interoceptive Exposure is when you provoke sensational or physical symptoms associated with a threat. So, you're deliberately triggering symptoms associated with the "fight or flight" response to eventually desensitize yourself toward the feelings that it gives you. Some examples would be provoking an increase in your heart rate, shortness of breath, or dizziness, and then maintaining contact with the feared sensation until it goes away. This type of exposure therapy works great for those suffering from panic attacks.

Remember when I was telling you to get sassy with your brain. This is the best time to do it. Interoceptive exposure would have you provoke scary panicky sensations and then sit with it, observing the feelings, thoughts, and emotions they give you. Evaluate the whole situation from start to finish. How the scary sensations started and how they slowly went away when your body started to relax.

Here are some exercises to provoke the symptoms:

1. **Racing heart** - Sprint for a short period of time to get your heart rate elevated. Now stop to feel the sensations. Acknowledge the fact that you didn't have a heart attack and die.

48

2. **Perspiration** - Do an aerobic exercise or sit in a sauna. Allow yourself to sweat and sit with it. Notice that the sweat is your body's response to cool itself down as a result of an increase in temperature.

3. **Shortness of breath or throat tightening** - Sprint for a short period of time or provoke hyperventilation through rapid deep breathing for 1 minute. You can also try to swallow quickly for up to 10 times, or straw breath for 45 seconds. Experience the sensations that occur during hyperventilation and notice how your body eventually regulates itself. You didn't pass out and you didn't die.

4. **Dizziness** - Sit in an office chair and spin around for 1 minute or turn around in circles while standing. Let yourself experience the sensations once you stop. Take notice of how you regained control again.

5. **Lightheadedness** - Hold your breath for 45 seconds to 1 minute. Notice how your breathing becomes regular again and how your body alters itself to get the oxygen it needs.

6. **Nausea** - You can try placing your head below your heart, such as between your legs while bending down. Stay there for 1 minute and come up slowly. Notice a nauseous disorientating feeling. Some other sensations that can occur are warmness in the face or rapid heartbeat.

Turn these scary situations into something funny. Force yourself to laugh, pretend to faint, or pretend you are an A list celebrity acting out a death scene. Look in the mirror and observe your facial reactions. Do you have a scared look on your face? If so, try to smile, laugh at yourself, make fun of the pouty scared face you're making. Do whatever you need to do to show your bossy brain that you're not scared.

Expose Yourself Through Virtual Reality

Virtual reality simulates real life or fictional 3-D interactive experiences in which you're entirely immersed in the situation. VR is an excellent tool to use for exposure therapy because it allows you to gradually expose yourself to your fear. The process can also be repeated as often as needed to overcome the fear. You can gradually expose yourself to your fear and progressively increase the intensity as you feel comfortable. VR can be super effective, and it can be used in a controlled, safe environment. It provides a personal experience that feels more realistic because you feel completely immersed in the situation.

VR can be done by yourself or with the help of a therapist. A VR headset is fairly inexpensive and can be purchased online if you'd like to try it out for yourself. You can tailor your games so that you're exposing yourself to your feared situation. Try to approach exposure gradually at only a mildly uncomfortable pace.

Retrain The Emotional Amygdala

Exposure therapy is meant to retrain the highly emotional amygdala which is the part of the brain responsible for the "flight or fight" response. The amygdala is a subconscious part of your brain that doesn't require any thinking. Its job is to react quickly, giving you all the strength you need in order to overcome a perceived threat.

The amygdala doesn't rely on logic or reason, it only operates on what it has learned from past experiences. This is why some children who are bitten by dogs develop a phobia towards dogs in the future. The fear gets stored in the amygdala, which now associate's dogs with being a threat. The amygdala now triggers the "fight or flight" response each time a dog is around. It's using past experiences rather than rational, which is why trying to talk yourself out of a fearful situation doesn't work. The idea is that you have to retrain your brain to not fear these non-threatening situations in the future. The amygdala is usually on autopilot or standby until there is a fearful situation that requires its assistance.

The best time to retrain the amygdala is when it's fully active so the new memory of the event gets stored. Each time you expose yourself to the same fear and change your reaction, your amygdala will store this new information. It will then alter its reaction for when the situation presents itself in the future. This is why it's so important to face your fears head on. Avoiding it only reassures your amygdala that your fear is an actual threat. The person with the dog phobia will need to slowly expose themselves to dogs and sit with the fear long enough or repeatedly to retrain their amygdala. While sitting with the fear, they can use affirmations, such as "I am strong, I am not scared, dogs are safe and friendly." Repeating powerful fear rebuking phrases can really help retrain the brain. You must repeat these phrases with conviction and really believe them to be true.

When I was younger, I experienced a fainting sensation while watching a movie at the theater. I didn't know what was happening, so I ran to the bathroom to splash water on my face. I was terrified at the possibility of it happening again, so I sat outside waiting for my friends to come out. From then on, I avoided movie theaters at all costs. My fear of fainting started to get worse. I eventually started to avoid any outing that required a dimly lit room and the need to focus on one particular thing. I began carrying a water bottle with me at all times so I could splash water on my face in case a fainting sensation came along.

By avoiding these situations, I was only intensifying the fear by feeding into my bossy brain's narrative. It got to the point where my "fight or flight" response would kick in any time a friend would even suggest watching a movie. This fear turned into such a drag, and it really started to affect my social life. This is when I turned to alcohol to help me relax in social situations. I noticed that alcohol would take my fear away in the "moment." I emphasize "moment" because the next day my anxiety would come back 100 x worse. Alcohol became my social crutch and eventually I wasn't able to go out with friends without it. I would avoid sober situations just to avoid the possibility of having another panic attack.

Avoiding sober events was training my brain to view being sober as a threat. This went on for many years. My fear had taken itself to a new level. I knew I had to sober up and face these fears in order to feel normal again. I started by taking walks with friends or going to the gym together. Then I started to attend a few sober outings, but only committed to stay for a short period of time. If a panicky feeling came over me, I would tell myself to feel it and flow through it as much as possible. I tried my hardest not to run to the bathroom if the sensation occurred. Each time I resisted the urge to leave, the fear would diminish more and more. Once I started gaining control, I was able to start going out without my water bottle next to me. Every sober event that I went to was an opportunity to retrain my brain. The more uncomfortable I felt, the better, because it was in this uncomfortableness that I was able to shift my fear into strength. I would let myself feel the anxiety and work its way through me. Each time I did this, I would feel myself getting stronger and stronger, until the fear was no longer a factor.

Biofeedback

Biofeedback teaches the anxious person to control their physiological response related to anxious thoughts. Every time someone experiences an anxious thought, the body releases stress hormones, which prepares the body for "fight or flight." Biofeedback gives the person control by allowing them to hear and see their physiological responses once an anxious thought has been triggered. This would include heart rate, rapid or shallow breathing, muscle tension, body temperature, brain waves, and metabolic activity.

Essentially, biofeedback increases your awareness as to what's going on in your body while you're experiencing anxiety. Then, relaxation techniques are used to help manage these symptoms. By watching your bodily responses while you try to control and manage them, you're able to see what works and what doesn't. Using this technique over and over again retrains your brain on how to better manage your anxious or stressful thoughts in the future.

Biofeedback can be done at a clinic, or the bio-monitoring equipment can be rented to do in comfort of your home.

Neurofeedback

Someone with anxiety may experience excessive brain wave activity on the right side of the brain while neglecting the left side. Brain waves could also be firing off in the wrong area of the brain under certain circumstances. Neurofeedback is a type of biofeedback that focuses on balancing out these brain wave patterns by using computer technology. Neurofeedback is able to measure these waves through brain mapping. The person will have electrodes placed on their head and they'll be given a video to watch which will stimulate brain wave activity. Think of the video as a video game. The video will be controlled based on how the person responds to it, in order to get a desired response. The video might be something like a roller coaster, which will show a visual of the coaster accelerating if your brain waves are on point or a visual of black smoke if your brain waves are out of whack. By being able to witness yourself physically control your brain, you're able to train your brain to think in better ways. There are affordable devices you can purchase online for less than $200, or you can have this professionally done at a clinic.

The at home biofeedback device would be something like a headband placed over your forehead. It would measure brain activity, heart rate, breathing, and body movements. The at home device is commonly used for measuring your relaxation response during meditation, but it can be used during other activities as well. This device would be especially useful when combined with imaginal, and interoceptive exposure therapy. Just a quick reminder that imaginal exposure therapy is when you use visualization techniques or a written script to overcome fears or phobias. Interoceptive exposure therapy is when you provoke bodily sensations, such as deliberately increasing your heart rate, in order to desensitize yourself toward these sensations during a panic attack. Using the device while utilizing relaxation techniques, combined with exposure therapy can help you monitor your success. It does this by letting you know how well you're controlling your brain activity during the "fight or flight" response. The biofeedback device would also work great when paired with virtual exposure therapy, as long as you can somehow fit both devices on your head. I know it may seem overwhelming, but these techniques have been proven very successful with lasting results, so it's worth a try.

Chapter 4: In a Nutshell

1. Expose yourself to your fears through exposure therapy. Most people with anxiety use avoidance tactics to protect themselves. What they may not realize is that avoidance is only strengthening their fear. The only way to diminish the fear is to face it head on. There are 3 types of methods that can be used. Imaginal, in vivo, and interoceptive exposure.

    a. **Imaginal Exposure** involves imagining, writing and reading the person's trauma memory or most feared scenario. This process of engagement, visiting or revisiting, and processing is repeated over and over again in order to diminish the fear.

    b. **In Vivo Exposure** involves confrontation techniques, rather than visuals or imagination. In vivo uses real world scenarios of feared stimuli. Someone with PTSD may have a fear of objects, people, or places. In vivo exposure would have the person expose themselves in real life to these feared situations.

    c. **Interoceptive Exposure** is when you provoke sensational or physical symptoms associated with a threat, such as increasing your heart rate, shortness of breath, or dizziness, and then maintaining contact with the feared sensation until it subsides. This will diminish the person's fear associated with the "fight or flight" response.

2. Virtual reality equipment can be used to provide a more real-life experience when using Imaginal and in vivo exposure.

3. Biofeedback is a technique that enables the person to gain more control of their "fight or flight" response. This can be done by using neurofeedback techniques that can measure performance through a video game like atmosphere. This allows the person to attempt to relax their bodily reactions by visually seeing and hearing how their body is responding.

Chapter 5: Stagnant Emotional Trauma

"If you are depressed, you are living in the past. If you are anxious, you are living in the future. If you are at peace, you are living in the present." Lao Tzu

When we do not acknowledge and release past emotional trauma, it can be carried around with us throughout life, remaining buried in our subconscious. If you often feel a strange enjoyment from pain, anger or negativity, it may mean that you're carrying around emotional baggage, only to be triggered at some point in the future.

<u>If you find that the following reflects your outlooks on life, then you're most likely carrying around stagnant emotional trauma:</u>

- Find comfort in being depressed
- Find comfort in isolating yourself from others
- Not grateful for anything in life
- Often living in the past
- Obsessing over the past
- Avoiding talking about or processing difficult challenges from the past
- Enjoy picking fights with people

- Constantly judging yourself or others
- Find it hard to have compassion toward others
- Find yourself experiencing resentment, agitation, sadness, rage, and impatience

Our memories help us learn and grow into the people we are today. Without them, growth would be impossible. It's when our past begins to take over our lives that it becomes a burden. You may not even think that you are carrying around this baggage, because it's hidden in your subconscious. You might tell yourself that you are happy, but your happiness may be coming from external factors and not genuinely from within. Holding onto emotional trauma stops you from finding true happiness, so we must learn how to let things go!

Acknowledging what this emotional trauma may be is the first step in releasing it. We must learn to forgive and forget the past in order to live in the present. Recall the quote at the beginning of this chapter. "If you are depressed, you are living in the past." The goal here is to get yourself to live in the present moment, keep an open mind, and start fresh so that you can accumulate more positive emotions. When you let go of old baggage that no longer serves you, it makes room for new opportunities.

Imagine a hoarder who has an intense fear of letting go of physical objects. They continue to collect objects, never getting rid of old ones, only to keep piling things over things. The hoarder's irrational need to keep collecting old baggage is easily spotted from an outsider, while those harboring emotional trauma are not so obvious, especially to the person holding it. In both cases, the person is holding onto something that is no longer serving them, which is cluttering up their world. The hoarder may justify that the reason for holding onto these things are for sentimental value, potential future value, or simply because they cannot let things go. They can accumulate so many things to the point where they can barely walk around in their own house. At some point, their house becomes so overwhelming that they develop pest infestations, mold toxicity, and dry rot from all the clutter and food scraps. Accumulated perpetual emotional baggage is the same idea, except instead of pests, mold and dry rot, you can end up with anxiety, depression, and other mental health issues.

These suppressed emotions tend to reveal themselves when triggered by a similar experience or while intoxicated. Alcohol can trigger suppressed emotions by bringing back memories related to trauma, and the feelings associated with them. Alcohol intensifies emotions, which is why it makes you feel really good when you're in a good mood, and really bad when you're in a bad mood. Sometimes people use alcohol to numb their pain, which seems to work in the moment, only for the pain to come back even worse the next day. If you find yourself angry, sad, crying, or thinking about the past while drinking, then you're most likely holding onto emotional baggage.

Another way of understanding this concept is by imagining a bodily injury that causes scar tissue. Once I punctured my finger with a knife when I was trying to pit an avocado. I refused to go to the hospital even though my finger was gushing blood. The wound turned into scar tissue, leaving a large lump on my finger. Now, every time something scrapes against it, there is an intense pain that shoots through my finger. The problem was that I did not deal with the circumstance at the moment it occurred. I just covered it up with a bandage. Had I gone to the doctor, they would have stitched it up, and the wound would have healed properly. Instead, I will hold onto this lump for the rest of my life, causing me pain each time I accidentally hit it on something. The great news is that I can have the scar tissue removed, which will eliminate any future pain. Likewise, it's possible to heal past emotional trauma through acknowledging when the negative emotion reveals itself and releasing it in a positive way.

Let's look at some signs to see if you may be living in the past. Do you...

- Think about the past often
- Find it hard to forgive others and enjoy seeking revenge
- Blame others, and play the victim often
- Find yourself saying that life isn't fair

- Hoard objects that no longer serve a purpose
- Impulsively speak or react to circumstances without thinking
- Feel the need to talk excessively, and not listen to what others have to say
- Often judge whether something is good or bad, rather than just letting things be
- Resist change in life
- Always think the worst in people or in life in general
- Try to control others rather than just accepting them for who they are
- Try to control circumstances and the outcome rather than just letting it be
- Have a hard time letting go of a toxic relationship
- Feel impatient, bored, frustrated, worried, depressed or anxious often
- Feel guilt or regret for something that's happened in the past

When dealing with the loss of a loved one, the person must allow themselves to mourn and release their emotions in a healthy way. Allow yourself to be sad, cry, and open up to others about how you're feeling. It's ok to distract yourself from the emotional pain, as long as you give yourself time to acknowledge that these emotions are there. The key is to acknowledge these emotions by expressing them rather than suppressing them. Suppressing emotions do not make them go away, they just get lodged in your subconscious as negative energy. The anger, resentment, and sadness you feel at a later time is a manifestation of these harbored emotions. If you choose to use alcohol, drugs, or find yourself clinging onto an unhealthy codependent relationship to cope with the emotional pain, then you are suppressing this emotion rather than dealing with it.

If you feel like you have stagnant emotional trauma, you can absolutely work through it at a later time by acknowledging the emotion, feeling the pain, and letting it go.

Here's how we can release stagnant emotional trauma

1. **Use a journal to identify and release any thoughts or emotions** that reveal themself during the process.

2. **Scan your childhood to see if any trauma could have occurred during this time**. Think back to a time in your childhood when you were happy, excited, and fearless. Then try to see if there was a time that you found it harder to feel these positive emotions. What could have possibly occurred around that time? Think about any significant or even insignificant events that could have changed your outlook on life during this period. Ask yourself what may have caused you fear in your childhood?

3. **Consider all the childhood memories you can remember** - If you find it hard to locate any emotional trauma, then try to find any memories that you can remember before the age of 13. There's a reason why your brain stored these memories, whether it may be good or bad. So, try to analyze each of these memories to see if they made you feel good, bad, safe or unsafe. If you find that any of these memories made you feel bad or unsafe, then these could be the culprits. It doesn't matter how insignificant you may determine these memories to be at this point in your life. They may have been significant when you were a child, and that's what matters the most here.

4. **Scan your adolescent years and adulthood** to see if you can locate any traumatic events that may have occurred. Continue to write any of your findings in your journal.

5. **Now revisit each memory** by taking the time to really feel and think of every detail that occurred during this event. Try to remember your surroundings, people's faces, the emotions you experienced, and thoughts you were thinking at the time. Think about how your outlook on life may have changed as a result of these events. Did it cause you to have a negative outlook on life? Really try to explore and feel everything about this time in your life. Keep doing this process with each traumatic event you've identified.

6. **Authentically feel these emotions** and if you find yourself feeling uncomfortable, sad, tense, or crying, then believe it or not, these are great signs. It means that you are working through and healing these emotions, which will free you of this burden you've been carrying around with you.

Children usually find strong negative emotions too hard to cope with, so they try not to feel them. Parents should guide their children on how to work through their emotions, especially if they're experiencing some type of traumatic event. Some examples are dealing with the death of a loved one, parents getting divorce, childhood abuse, abandonment issues, an alcoholic parent, or an illness a loved one may be experiencing. A child who is figuring themselves out sexually can also experience trauma if they have a family member who is outwardly homophobic. This type of behavior can cause the child to feel like there is something wrong with them, resulting in a lack of self-esteem and self-confidence, which can manifest into social anxiety or other mood disorders later in life.

The global pandemic we're currently going through can have damaging effects on the younger generations. It is important to talk to children to get them to work through emotions they may be experiencing as a result of the pandemic. Be honest with them, because children sense and pick up on their parents fears and emotions. Just because they don't talk about their feelings, doesn't mean they're not feeling them. Children are good at suppressing their emotions. You might be able to tell if your child is suppressing their emotions if they are displaying moodiness, fearfulness, and are socially withdrawal.

The best thing you can do for your children is live in the present moment, because if you are living in the present, you are at peace, regardless of the situation you are in. Create a good example for your children, because they are always actively watching, processing, and storing everything around them, which includes emotions felt by others.

My mother suffered from hypochondria ever since she was a little girl, which started after her mother's death. She was only 16 years old when she lost her mom to ovarian cancer, and she watched her suffer for over 2 years. My mom was terrified at the idea of succumbing to her mother's same fate and developed hypochondria as a result of it. My grandfather was more of a tough love type of guy, rather than a coddler, so she didn't have an adult who could help her work through these emotions. Now this fear has been passed down to her own children and will continue to be passed down until the emotions are dealt with.

Here are some questions you can ask your children to get them to open up

1. How does this situation make you feel?
2. Are you feeling angry, sad, upset, happy?
3. What worries or scares you about this situation?

The point is to keep asking questions to get your child to deal with the emotions they may be feeling. You can start by asking lighthearted questions, while working your way up to more emotional ones. This way you can make your child feel comfortable and safe, while opening up at their own pace.

Post-Traumatic Stress Disorder (PTSD)

Post-traumatic stress disorder is more easily identified because the person exhibits an intense fear associated with the emotional trauma.

PTSD is a disorder that can occur in people as a result of some type of traumatic event. It could be an event that happened to them personally or that they witnessed happening to someone else. These traumatic events are usually easier to pinpoint, and they can consist of experiencing war, killing or witnessing the killing of others, natural disasters, terrorism, rape, near death experiences, being robbed, or losing a loved one in a violent way. The traumatic event can also be as simple as briefly losing a parent while out in public. The common denominator in all of these traumatic events is the compromise of one's trust and security.

Most people who experience a traumatic event will suffer from acute stress disorder, which they will likely recover from within 30 days. However, those predisposed to anxiety, depression, or prior trauma are at a higher risk of developing PTSD.

People with PTSD experience long lasting disturbing recurring thoughts, feelings, and dreams related to their traumatic experience. They can continue to relive these experiences through flashbacks, nightmares, and phobias. They may experience involuntary intrusive thoughts and images of the event over and over again.

As a result, someone with PTSD may experience depression, panic attacks, sadness, fear, anger, loneliness, detachment from others, and sensitivity to loud noises or unexpected touch. To cope with the stress, one might resort to self-medicating through alcohol, drugs, or food.

Symptoms of PTSD

- **Untrusting of others** which is a coping mechanism meant to protect themselves against any further harm or abuse.

- **Abandonment of faith** because they can't understand how this trauma was allowed to happen to them. Especially if they believe they are good people.

- **Loneliness and detachment** from others and finding it hard to connect.

- **Flashbacks** that include reliving the trauma visually through physical sensations that include pain or discomfort, as well as emotional trauma in which the person feels the same emotions that they felt during the traumatic event.

- **Hypervigilance** about people and their surroundings. Studying people's actions, words, noises, movements, and other things in their surroundings.

- **Self-blame or shamefulness** wondering if it's something they did or didn't do to bring the traumatic experience onto themselves.

- **Constantly strategizing different scenarios** on how they could have prevented the incident or handled it differently.

- **Avoiding people, places, activities, and situations** that can trigger memories of the traumatic event. They may avoid talking about the event as well.

- **Inner child issues** that manifest into emotional blocks and stunted personal growth later in life.

- **Experiencing depression, anxiety, or some other type of mood disorder**.

- **Chronic pain** as a result of muscle armoring which is constantly keeping their body in a defense mode ready for "fight or flight".

Techniques to Overcome PTSD

1. **Inner child work**, which we will explore in the next section.

2. **Anything that involves reducing stress and anxiety**, such as yoga, meditation, massage, finding positive distractions that help stimulate your brain, such as puzzles, and exercise.

3. **Using exposure therapy** that involves any of the following:

   - **Imaginal Exposure** involves imagining, writing and reading the person's trauma memory or most feared scenario.

This process of engagement, revisiting, and processing is repeated over and over again in order to diminish the fear.

- **In Vivo Exposure** involves confrontation techniques, rather than visuals or imaginary exposure. In vivo uses real world scenarios of feared stimuli. Someone with PTSD may have a fear of objects, people, or places. In vivo exposure would have the person expose themselves in real life to these feared scenarios.

- **Interoceptive Exposure** is when you provoke sensational or physical symptoms associated with a threat, such as increasing your heart rate, shortness of breath, or dizziness, and then maintaining contact with the feared sensation until it subsides. This will diminish the person's fear associated with the "fight or flight" response.

I believe that I experienced PTSD as a result of my cousin's sudden death when I was 11 years old. I saw her 2 weeks prior to her aneurysm, and she seemed perfectly healthy, so I couldn't understand how she could suddenly collapse and die. I was told she was at work one day suffering from an intense headache and suddenly passed out after experiencing an aneurysm. Later that evening she lapsed into a coma, which eventually led to her passing.

I kept replaying this story in my head to try to make sense of it. I had already suffered from hypochondria leading up to this traumatic event, but I believe this manifested into a form of PTSD. I had never worried about suddenly falling to my death or fainting, but this developed into a recurring debilitating fear that lasted for almost 16 years. The only way I overcame it was actually experiencing fainting for my first time. I had never fainted in my life, so I didn't know what to expect. Once it finally happened, it was nothing like what I thought it would be. I fainted as a result of dehydration and being exposed to a sauna for a long period of time. It was actually an oddly pleasant feeling of sudden tiredness that didn't involve fear. I just had to let go and let it happen.

So why was I catastrophizing fainting as if I would die if it actually happened? This was the logic that helped me overcome my fear. The act of actually experiencing the fear helped desensitize me toward it.

Although PTSD is classified as anyone who has been experiencing symptoms for over a month, I believe most of us have some sort of acute stress that we may be holding onto. Scan through your childhood to see if you can identify any traumatic events that you may have experienced. The event can be as simple as losing your parents at the grocery store for 5 minutes. This may seem insignificant, however in those 5 minutes, a child's security and safety was compromised. These emotional memories can be stored in your subconscious and can manifest into unhealthy attachment issues, such as separation anxiety or codependent relationships in adulthood. One may not even realize that this is a form of PTSD, and that their unhealthy attachments most likely stemmed from a traumatic childhood experience. Inner child work can really benefit someone suffering from PTSD, social anxiety, or codependency.

Work With Your Inner Child

The inner child is the part of your psyche that maintains the innocence, happiness, excitement, creativity and imagination throughout life. The inner child is the part of your personality that is mostly related to your subconscious mind. It's a byproduct of your childhood years. Humans acquire our sense of belonging, love and safety early on in life. Children who experience emotional trauma or dysfunction within the family can develop blockages when it comes to these innocent inner child emotions. In the first 5 - 7 years of life, children are in somewhat of a hypnotic state. They take in all types of visuals and information like a sponge. This is when the programming begins and it's tough to change later in life. During these early years, the child is developing order and structure by observing those around them, such as family members and caretakers. Any emotional trauma or family dysfunction that occurs in this stage of life will be programmed in the psyche and will remain there until it's acknowledged, forgiven, and healed. Blaming your parents or caretakers will not release this trauma, it will actually make it worse.

You must be able to forgive in order to overcome it. You should also try to understand that if your parents were the cause of your emotional trauma, then they are most likely victims of their own childhood.

My parents raised me with nothing but love, affection, and protection, which led me to live a very happy childhood. My inner child trauma lies with my mother and her anxiety related issues which I witnessed at a very young age. I felt safe when it came to belonging, love, and family security, but I didn't feel safe when it came to external physical factors, such as death or disease. I was 9 years old when my grandfather passed away from throat cancer and I clearly remember my mother running into the room hysterically crying and screaming that my grandfather had passed away. Seeing my mother's reaction gave me a terrifying fear of death, which compromised my sense of safety in the world. My mother doesn't handle bad news well and she's constantly worried that something bad will happen. Witnessing her behavior as a child made me fearful of the world as well.

I can't blame my mother for passing her worrisome anxious behavior to me, because she is a victim of her own childhood. She was only 16 when her mother passed away from ovarian cancer. She watched her suffer, getting surgery after surgery for almost 2 years before it took her life. Watching her mother go through this pain and suffering left her traumatized. Her father believed in tough love, so he did not comfort her in the way she needed in order to feel protected. She now sees the world as a dangerous place, which has compromised her sense of security. As a result, she became a hypochondriac and a control freak. She feels that if she doesn't control everything around her, something bad will happen.

Inner child work can help you regain your sense of security in the world. You can find a workshop or therapist that can help you work through the process. If this is something you would like to try on your own, you can use the following steps to guide you through it.

How to Heal Your Inner Child

Step 1 - Start by asking yourself the following questions:

1. Have you experienced any childhood trauma that you're aware of?

2. Did you feel safe or unsafe as a child?

3. Did you feel loved or neglected as a child?

4. Did you feel supported and accepted by your family and those around you?

5. Do you feel a sense of belonging within your immediate family?

6. Do you have healthy or unhealthy romantic relationships? This can trigger your inner child because relationships require intimacy and trust. This can threaten an inner child's safety by bringing back issues of abandonment or betrayal.

Step 2 - Now revisit your childhood memories and really try to get in sync with the emotions you felt as a child. Reparent your inner child in the way you wished your parents had done at the time. Note all your findings in a journal.

1. Use visualization techniques to meet and reparent your inner child.

2. Now be your own parent or protector. You can show your inner child love, affection, and safety. You can do this by visualizing yourself comforting and caring for your inner child.

3. You can also write a letter from your inner child explaining how this trauma made you feel, as well as the love, affection, and safety you wish to seek now.

4. You can share your pain or hurt with someone you trust, such as a family member, friend, or therapist. Talking about your findings and emotions can help you work through the process.

5. Declare your self-worth and provide a sense of safety by speaking loving and supporting affirmations throughout the day. The idea is to have these affirmations reprogram your subconscious mind.

Inner Child Visualization Process

Begin the process with a relaxing meditation to get into a peaceful, safe place. You can do this by sitting upright or lying down, just make sure you don't fall asleep. I'd suggest using an eye mask to help kick start the relaxation process. Start by taking deep relaxing breaths. With each exhale, find yourself becoming more, and more relaxed. Tense all the muscles in your body for 5 seconds and then release. You can repeat this tensing and releasing as many times as you need in order to get your muscles to relax. I find it helpful to feel myself being pulled to the earth by gravity with a warm sparkling light shining on my body.

Now that you're in a meditative state with a clear mind, remember a moment in time when you were a child and felt traumatized, hurt or scared. In this time, you felt alone, and didn't have anyone to turn to. Or it could be that you just didn't want to share these feelings with those around you. When you find the image of your inner child, be an observer of the situation. Do not become the inner child. Visualize the surroundings in this moment in time. Was it indoor or outdoor? What did the walls look like? What kind of plants were surrounding you? Was it day or night? Who was with you and what were they doing?

If there is an abusive adult in the situation, first focus your attention on the adult and tell them to stop. Tell them that what they are doing is wrong and that they need to leave. This can involve verbal abuse, as well as abuse toward another parent or child. Show this inner child that they are protected and have nothing to fear anymore.

Now visualize yourself as a strong, healthy adult. Comfort the inner child by hugging them and telling them they are safe now. Earn the child's trust by showing them that they are safe, and there's nothing to be scared of anymore. Show them that you love them and will never leave them. Be nurturing toward the inner child, hold them, and rock them in your arms.

Once you gain the trust of your inner child, visualize both of you becoming one. Your inner child is now with you in a safe place forever. That old memory is empty and can't hurt them anymore.

Now it's time to become that innocent, creative, joyful, happy, and excited child you once were. Visualize a time in your early childhood when you felt these emotions. This should be a time before you began to see the world as a harmful place. If you find it hard to imagine a time when you felt the world was harmless, then visualize yourself as an infant coming into this world. Notice your big curious eyes, the excitement, curiosity and joyfulness you feel coming into this world. Let these emotions penetrate your body, right down to your bones. Live it, feel it, and make it your reality moving forward.

Here are some affirmations you can use to heal your inner child

- The world is a loving and safe place!
- I am loved by those around me!
- I am fierce, fearless, and a badass!
- I am healthy and strong!
- I am destined to live a long and healthy life!
- The universe is a safe place filled with love!
- The universe loves and supports me!
- I look forward to my future!
- My past is behind me, and my present is awesome!
- I am healed, and my mind is strong!
- I love and accept myself for who I am!
- I am happy and filled with joy!

Free Yourself from Judgement

"When you judge another, you do not define them, you define yourself." - *Wayne Dyer*

A child who experiences emotional trauma or dysfunction when they are young, especially feelings of neglect, can develop into self-esteem issues. This can lead to social anxiety. Social anxiety goes hand in hand with ego and involves judgements toward yourself and others.

Judgement about yourself, life experiences, and others, promotes stress, sadness, anger, and separateness, while having a significant impact on anxiety and depression. Self-judgement can have an effect on self-confidence, leading to unhappiness, while passing judgement toward others creates unnecessary stress.

Sometimes stressful life experiences are inevitable, but it's how we react to them that's important. Negative thoughts, such as "playing the victim" "name calling" "justifying who's right and who's wrong" doesn't matter because you're only hurting yourself in the end. "Resentment is like taking poison and waiting for the other person to die." Think of this quote next time you find yourself holding onto anger toward someone else. Try to look at the situation from the other person's perspective. You may not know the reason someone may be acting a certain way. That person who nudges you slightly out of the way because they are trying to leave the grocery store. They may be experiencing a panic attack. That person stuck in traffic, honking their horn for someone to move out of the way, could be experiencing claustrophobia in their car. That waiter that was slightly rude to you, may have experienced a loss of a loved one. You just don't know, so rather than pass judgement toward others, just remain neutral.

Also, take a moment to examine why you may feel the need to judge others. Could it be because it's something you dislike about yourself? Could it be that you are doing it to make yourself feel superior? Could it be that you are judging others to distract people from judging you?

Treat everyone how you would like to be treated. Treat everyone how you would like them to treat your loved ones. TRUST when I say that you will benefit greatly from having this attitude. How they act and feel does not matter. What's important is how you react to the situation.

So how do you know if you are passing judgement? Well, first of all, what is judgement? Judgement involves forming an opinion (good or bad) around two facts and believing your opinion to be true. You can differentiate fact from opinion by determining whether emotion is involved. Opinions involve emotion while facts do not. A fact is proven to be true, and it doesn't involve interpretation.

Here are some examples of facts vs judgements:

1. Stating that a leaf is green is a fact because it can be visibly seen. There's no emotion behind it. It just is what it is. Saying the leaf is beautiful is a judgement, because it may seem beautiful to you, but maybe not to someone else. This involves emotion as you may wonder why the other person doesn't agree with you.

2. Stating that rain makes you wet is a fact, while saying rain is depressing is a judgement.

3. Stating that the sun is out today is a fact, while saying it's a beautiful day is a judgement.

Here are some examples of passing judgement onto others:

1. Fearing that your friends are gossiping about you while they whisper and look at you from a distance, is passing judgement. They may actually be gossiping about you, but you do not know this for a fact.

2. If you feel like someone is judging you, that means that you are judging them.

3. Telling a friend that they always have to have an opinion about something is passing judgement.

4. If you pass by someone gossiping about someone else and think to yourself, "wow, that person gossips a lot," you are passing judgement.

5. Shaking your head at someone experiencing road rage is passing judgement.

<u>Here are some examples of passing judgement onto yourself:</u>

1. Telling yourself that you look fat in your outfit is passing judgement.

2. Telling yourself that you're weak because you have anxiety is passing judgement.

3. Replaying something in your head that you regret saying, is passing judgement.

Do you see where I am going here with these examples? We're all guilty of passing judgement, and we will most likely do it again at some point in the future. But it's important to always be mindful of our thoughts and actions that might be causing us unhappiness, unnecessary stress, anxiety, and depression.

Allowing things to just be is so much more powerful than having a reaction or an opinion. This is not to say that having an opinion while conversating is not ok. You just need to ask yourself if offering your opinion is really necessary, or if it will trigger an unnecessary argument. If you find that you would be better off not offering your opinion, then don't do it! Just be a listener. Being mindful of how your actions impact others will break down their defenses, resulting in them treating you the same way that you treat them. This is a win-win as it creates healthier relationships and less stress in your life.

The Judgy Social Anxiety

People who experience social anxiety have an overwhelming persistent fear of social situations that might cause them to be judged, humiliated, rejected, or the center of attention. This person may avoid social situations that are important for self-growth, such as meeting new people, job interviews, and normal day to day activities which can become very debilitating.

What's interesting about social anxiety is that the person's biggest fear is being judged by others, but what they don't realize is that they are the ones doing most of the judging. Someone who is characterized as having a big ego is usually someone who exudes confidence and is more extroverted. On the other hand, someone who is shy may be characterized as being reserved, and more of a listener rather than a talker. The twist is that someone with social anxiety may exhibit more egotistical behavior than the more confident person. The idea lies in the fact that shyness is usually covering up some type of insecurity coming from within. The shy person may desire the confidence to be more outgoing, but their fear of judgement stops them from being this way. Also, their fear of being judged, means they are judging others for judging them. They also judge themselves often, and then judge themselves for judging themselves. Do you see what I'm saying? A lot of unnecessary judging going on here. All this judging can get extremely exhausting and creates separateness, which leads to sadness, depression, and anxiety. Separating yourself from others by judging whether they are better or worse than you is a form of ego. Not only are you judging others, but you are also judging yourself.

Techniques to Overcome Social Anxiety

1. **Inner child work** - Since social anxiety is usually closely linked with childhood emotional trauma, Inner child work would be a great way to overcome this fear. This type of therapy consists of

healing unresolved trauma that remains stagnant in the body. Inner child issues can stunt someone's self-growth, which could result in underdeveloped social skills. Identifying, acknowledging, and healing this trauma can help build confidence in oneself, thereby reducing one's fear of judgement. Refer back to the Inner Child section to see how you can use this process to overcome social anxiety.

2. **Retrain your brain to shift negative thoughts to positive thoughts**, especially when it comes to yourself. First acknowledge when you have a negative thought. Every time you acknowledge the negative thought, you are lessening its strength. Refrain from talking down to yourself or playing the victim. Instead, use positive self-affirmations to lift yourself up. Some examples might be: "I am strong! I am fearless! I am loved! I am worthy! I am awesome!" Saying these things to yourself does not make you conceited. It's a way of building self-image and self-worth to provide you with the confidence you need in social situations. Repetitively saying and feeling these things about yourself can really have an impact on how you feel inside.

3. **Change your perspective by looking at the situation from a third person's point of view**. Is the situation as bad as you think? Is everyone really looking at you? Is everyone really judging you? Try to look at these situations in a different perspective. Could it be that the person looking at you is just admiring your outfit? Or could it be that the person asking you questions is genuinely interested in getting to know you? Could it be that the person who you thought was mocking you was actually laughing with you? Or could it be that the person's comment that you were offended by wasn't actually meant to be offensive, but was actually meant to be a joke?

4. **Exposure therapy** would involve gradually exposing yourself to your feared social situation. This could include eating at restaurants, using public bathrooms, hanging with friends, going to social events, or public speaking. Gradually exposing yourself

to your fears actually helps diminish them. You can revisit the Exposure Yourself Chapter to learn how to apply this technique.

Learn to release the ego, be present, and feel the oneness with those around you. Biologically we are all made up of the same 4 elements, which are hydrogen, oxygen, carbon, and nitrogen. We're all here temporarily and will someday transition over. In the end, does it really matter? Think back to an embarrassing moment that you experienced in childhood or high school. Does that moment in time matter to you now? When you look at it from today's perspective, I'm sure it seems pretty insignificant, right? Now think of a moment in time when you were really happy. Does that moment really matter to you now? Probably not. What should matter to you now is the present moment. Next time you fear being judged, remember that we are all the same, made up of the same 4 elements. We all exhibit the same basic emotions which are happiness, sadness, fear and anger. Make a conscious effort to live in the present moment and look at others as your equivalent. Don't idolize or look down on people. Remember that in the end, we are all one, made up of eternal energy.

Chapter 5: In a Nutshell

1. Past emotional trauma that is not dealt with and released in a proper way remains in the human body as negative energy. This energy can manifest into depression and anxiety, which reveals itself through anger and negativity later in life. The only way to release this stagnant emotional trauma is to expose it, feel it, and release it.

2. Inner child trauma involves experiencing something traumatic in early childhood. Children usually aren't good at releasing their emotions, so they need to have an adult help them work through it. Inner child work involves meeting and reparenting your inner child, which can help release lingering trauma.

3. We must learn to stop judging ourselves and those around us. Judgements only provoke anger, sadness, and separation. Allow

things to be as they are by staying neutral and accepting every circumstance you find yourself in.

Chapter 6: The Gut-Brain Axis

Back to Biology

Now that we know how to control our "fight or flight" response and release stagnant emotional trauma, let's explore what's going on inside our body and how to heal it. I'm going to take you back to biology in this chapter. I know it may feel like a drag, but it's important to understand how your body works, in order to fix it. So put your thinking caps on and it will be done before you know it. Promise! Then we'll see what we need to do to detox and nourish our body in order to take control of our bossy brain.

There is a close connection between the brain and gut known as the gut-brain axis. The human gut has its own nervous system, which is called the enteric nervous system. It's lined with 50 - 100 million nerve cells that communicate to the brain through the vagus nerve, which we'll explore more in the next section. The gut is filled with thousands of sensors that collect information to send to the brain, such as food taste, fullness, satisfaction, hunger, nausea, and discomfort. This information sent from the gut is stored in the brain to use for decision making in the future. It reminds you about your prior experience with food. It will tell you whether you should have that hot dog that upset your stomach 2 weeks ago, or the habanero sauce that was too spicy.

All this information starts with the gut, sending it upward to the brain. The brain then sends signals back down to the gut telling it how to adjust its function based on the information provided. For example, if you ate some bad sushi, your gut would tell your brain that the sushi made you nauseous. Then the brain would tell the gut to vomit or to increase its intestinal contractions to remove the sushi quicker. But none of this could be done without the gut's intelligence. To put things into perspective, 90% of the information is sent from the gut to the brain, while only 10% is sent from the brain to the gut. Essentially, the gut is carrying this relationship, so we need to give it a little more credit. As a matter of fact, the gut can do most of its work without the brain. This is why the gut is sometimes referred to as the "second brain."

Not only does the gut provide information, but it's also where our body extracts important vitamins and minerals. The gut is also where our body produces the happy chemicals, serotonin and dopamine. These are incredibly important to maintain healthy brain function, so imagine how an unhealthy gut can affect this relationship.

An Unhealthy Gut Can Lead to Malnutrition

Our bodies need to have a certain number of vitamins and minerals to function properly. Any slight deficiency can throw the body out of balance, potentially resulting in mental health challenges. The most important vitamins and minerals needed to keep your bossy brain in check, are magnesium, B vitamins, zinc, vitamin D3, and iron. The gut has good and bad microbiota that keeps it going. Dysbiosis is when the bad guys take over the good guys. Dysbiosis combined with poor nutrition makes it harder for your intestines to absorb nutrients from your food. If you're not absorbing enough nutrients from the food you're eating, it can lead to malnutrition, which can promote anxiety. This is why it's so it's important to try to rebalance your gut bacteria as soon as possible.

Here are some signs that you may have an unhealthy gut:

1. **Digestive issues** - such as continuously experiencing an upset stomach, gas, bloating, constipation, diarrhea, and abdominal pain.

2. **Sugar and carbohydrates** are what the bad guys feed on, so if you are having these cravings, that means there's too many of these bad critters in your digestive tract.

3. **Skin issues** such as rashes, acne, eczema, and psoriasis are all associated with inflammation that is closely linked to an unhealthy gut.

4. **Allergies** such as food, respiratory, and skin allergies.

5. **Frequent infections** such as sinus infections, yeast infections, and UTIs are all signs that the bad guys have taken over the good guys.

6. **Sleep disturbances** or fatigue can be a result of a lack of serotonin produced by the intestines. Serotonin is responsible for keeping us awake, as well as allowing us to sleep, and 90% of it is produced in the gut. Any imbalance can affect the production and distribution of this happy chemical.

7. **Mood disorders** are often linked to an unhealthy gut, and those who suffer from anxiety and depression have shown improvements after taking a daily probiotic.

8. **Autoimmune disorders** such as lupus, rheumatoid arthritis, celiac disease, type 1 diabetes, and multiple sclerosis are all conditions in which the immune system attacks healthy cells. An abundance of bad guys in the gut compromises the immune system, which could be the reason for the immune dysfunction in these diseases. Someone who has any of these conditions should

consider taking a daily probiotic, which will boost their immune system.

If you have any of these symptoms, you should try some type of detox to bring your gut microbiota back into balance. Some detoxes you can try are juice cleanses, fasting, liver detox, colon detox, or simply food restrictions. While detoxing, you should include some type of probiotic to repopulate the gut with the good guys. You can also further the detox by getting colonics or using an enema at home. I know! Gross, right? But these can really help you get the old gunk out!

The Microbiome

So, let's learn more about what these little microbiotas do in our body. The microbiome consists of trillions of microorganisms and thousands of different species, which include bacteria, fungi, parasites, and viruses. Everyone's microbiome is unique and contains different amounts of microbiota. The richer and more diverse the microbiota is in your gut, the lower your risk of mental health issues. You develop this microbiota starting in your mother's womb and the first 3 years of life. This is why it is so important for pregnant women to heal any digestive issues and have a diet rich in healthy foods. An expecting mother who is malnourished can predispose her unborn child to mental health challenges later in life without even realizing it.

Here are some ways you can increase the healthy bacteria in your gut:

- Take a probiotic supplement, drink kefir milk, or eat yogurt
- Eat fermented foods like kimchi or sauerkraut
- Eat prebiotic fiber like chicory, garlic, onions, or inulin
- Reduce your intake of sugar and artificial sweeteners
- Reduce stress, get enough sleep, and exercise
- Avoid taking antibiotics if possible
- Limit alcohol, carbohydrates, processed and fried foods

- Don't be such a germaphobe. Some bacteria are actually healthy for your body because it builds up your immune system

So, now we know that there are good and bad guys that exist in our microbiome. These little critters can coexist perfectly fine as long as they are in balance, meaning there are more good guys than bad. If there is an imbalance caused by infections, illness or overuse of antibiotics, then the bad guys can get out of control. Imagine that there is a constant war going on in your gut. The good guys keep the bad guys in check. Now if the bad guys start to overtake the good guys, then this is when things can get out of whack. An overabundance of the bad guys can cause psychological problems as well as many other issues throughout the body. The good guys are responsible for keeping us relaxed, while promoting a sense of well-being by releasing GABA, which creates an anti-anxiety effect. They also help stimulate the vagus nerve, which gives you more control of your bossy brain.

The brain and gut have such a tight relationship, that a problem in the brain is almost always an indication of a problem in the gut. As you can now see, the nervous system is highly influenced by diet, which can influence everything from mood to obesity. This is why implementing a well-balanced healthy diet should be one of the first steps in getting control of the bossy brain.

Food Intolerance and The Elimination Diet

If you find that you might have an unhealthy gut, it is most likely linked to the food you are eating. Food intolerances have become more common in our day and age due to the overuse of certain ingredients in our food. Some of these ingredients include wheat, milk, soy, and corn. These ingredients are commonly found in prepackaged processed foods, as well as food prepared by restaurants. Food intolerances can also occur as a result of poor digestive health. The intolerant person's digestive tract is unable to digest and break down food, most likely due to an absence of an enzyme needed to fully digest the food.

It's important to determine what may be causing your food intolerance or digestive issues, so that you can bring your gut back into balance. The elimination diet is an excellent way to identify the culprit, eliminate it, and possibly reintroduce it at a later time. Note that food intolerances are different from food allergies. An allergy can cause dangerous reactions such as anaphylaxis, while an intolerance will only cause mild discomfort, such as gas, bloating, constipation, diarrhea, and skin rashes. If you find that you may have a food allergy, then consider getting an allergy test. You can purchase one online for a couple hundred dollars, or you can have your doctor do it for you.

An elimination diet starts by first narrowing down what you suspect might be causing your symptoms. Some common food sensitivities include dairy, gluten, corn, caffeine, sugar, peanuts, shellfish, eggs, red meat, chicken, soy, fructose, and wheat. It's important that you are extremely diligent in reading food labels before consuming them.

Steps in The Elimination Diet

1. **Eliminate** any foods that you suspect may be bothering you. You can also eliminate all the ingredients mentioned above for better results. This elimination phase should last around 2 - 3 weeks. If you notice that you are still experiencing symptoms, you may need to resort to an even stricter elimination list. Some other foods you may consider eliminating include fruits, veggies, tree nuts, seeds, legumes, butter, and spices. You could also try fasting for a day or two to help kick start the elimination process.

2. Once you are symptom free, you can **reintroduce** each food individually 2 - 3 days apart from one another. It's during this phase that you should pay close attention to whether your symptoms begin to reappear again and what food triggered it. Once you identify the culprit, you can eliminate it. You may be intolerant to more than one food, so continue reintroducing them at a slow pace.

3. By eliminating the culprit, you can allow your body to **heal**. Once your body heals, you may be able to reintroduce these foods back into your diet. This may take some time and everyone's tolerance is different, so look at this process as trial and error. Continue experimenting to figure out timing and whether reintroduction is even possible.

Here are some ways to avoid developing food sensitivities:

1. **Maintain a diversified diet** of many different types of foods. Avoid eating the same things over and over again.

2. **Prepare food yourself** rather than using packaged foods or going out to a restaurant.

3. **Avoiding excessive amounts of caffeine**.

4. **Take a digestive enzyme with each meal**. This will help with food breakdown and nutrient absorption.

5. **Buy organic** so you reduce your exposure to fungicides, pesticides, and herbicides.

6. **Breastfeeding** in early stages of life is extremely important in immune and digestive health. Breast milk contains colostrum, which is also known as nature's vaccine because of its high level of antibodies and white blood cells. **Colostrum** coats and seals the digestive tract, which helps protect against digestive issues, such as food sensitivities and allergies. Colostrum supplements can be taken at any age, and it can help jumpstart the healing process.

I get that most of us find it difficult to change our habits and stick with it, so let me give you a little secret on how to maintain a healthy diet. The first meal you have of the day should be the healthiest meal. This should consist of a smoothie, a juice, eggs with veggies, salad, kefir milk, or fruit, lightly sweetened granola, and plain yogurt. Don't start your day with sugary, high carb, fatty or fried foods. The reason this meal is so important is because it sets the tone for your cravings throughout the day. If you start your day with pancakes, donuts, or fried food, you will crave more sweet, fried, and unhealthy food throughout the day. I'm telling you; this trick really does work. You may find the most success by meal prepping the night before. Always have your healthy morning breakfast ready so that you don't splurge on an easy unhealthy alternative. Try this for at least a week and you will see what I'm talking about. Monitor your cravings based on what you eat in the morning.

Fecal Transplants

Ok, now you are starting to question my sanity, right? But yes, fecal transplants. It's a real thing, and I'm about to blow your mind!

A fecal transplant is when feces from a healthy donor is transplanted into an unhealthy recipient, which is usually accomplished through a colonoscopy or an enema. The purpose of the procedure is to promote new healthy bacteria growth in the recipient's unhealthy digestive tract. This procedure is most commonly used for treatment of recurrent C. diff colitis but can potentially help with other digestive related disorders as well.

Scientists are also seeing success in experiments with anxiety and depression related fecal transplants within mice. They're finding that transplanting feces from an extrovert mouse into a shy mouse, made the shy mouse act more like the extrovert mouse. They also found that transplanting feces from an obese mouse into lean mouse, made the lean mouse eat more like the obese mouse. Or get this, feces transferred from a stressed-out mouse into a relaxed mouse, made the relaxed mouse exhibit stressful behavior. Isn't that wild? Just by transplanting feces from one mouse to the next, made the recipient mouse exhibit the same behavior as the donor.

This indicates that mental and physical behavior can be altered based on the health of your gut's ecosystem. These new findings can shine light on new and groundbreaking treatments for depression, anxiety, and many other health challenges.

Revive the Vagus Nerve

Now let's go back to biology to explore the importance of the vagus nerve when it comes to anxiety. This nerve is the longest of the cranial nerves and is the main communication channel between the gut and brain. It's responsible for controlling functions related to the heart, lungs, and digestive tract. So, think about what happens when you have a panic attack. Your heart races, your breathing becomes shallow, and you have to run to the bathroom. The vagus nerve is what's controlling all of this. Having a healthy vagus nerve will mean that you have better control over your nervous system in times of panic. Since most of the information is communicated from the organs to the brain, it's important to keep the organs healthy, with the gut being one of them. An imbalance in the gut can distort communications to the brain, making it bossy.

The vagus nerve is responsible for stimulating every major organ in the body, which is why it's connected to so many different conditions, such as anxiety, depression, stress, inflammatory issues, epilepsy, adrenal fatigue, hormone imbalances, high blood pressure, cardiac issues, and the list goes on and on.

Here are some other reasons to strengthen your vagus nerve:

1. **Triggers your relaxation response** - The vagus nerve is responsible for bringing the body back into balance after the "fight or flight" response is triggered. It does this by releasing acetylcholine when it senses the presence of stress hormones. This tells your lungs to breathe, which promotes relaxation. Now imagine someone who is constantly stressed out or having anxiety. The vagus nerve would constantly be working at calming the body down, which can result in wear and tear, weakening the vagus nerve.

2. **Prevents inflammation** - The vagus nerve keeps inflammation in check by pumping out anti-inflammatory neurotransmitters when it senses inflammation. So, it's essentially regulating the body's immune response to a known trigger. Inflammation blocks the neural pathways making it harder to send signals so that the brain can function properly. This blockage also interferes with the production and transportation of the happy chemicals to the brain. So, it's very important to keep inflammation in check.

3. **Improves memory** - When the vagus nerve is stimulated, it releases hormones that activate the amygdala, which is where emotional memories are stored. This is why strengthening the vagus nerve could benefit those with degenerative diseases, such as Alzheimer's or dementia.

People with anxiety usually have a weak vagal tone because the vagus nerve is directly connected to emotional regulation. The good news is that you can engage, stimulate, and strengthen your vagal tone, leaving you better equipped to handle your bossy brain in the future. Strengthening your vagal tone can help you calm yourself down, reduce your heart rate, and breathe deeply, which would be especially helpful during moments of anxiety.

I know you're dying to know how to strengthen this super nerve, so here we go...

1. **Deep and slow breathing** - This can put you in a meditative state, which can suppress the "fight or flight" response while promoting relaxation. You can do this by counting 6 breaths over the course of a minute. Make sure you are breathing deeply and exhaling slowly.

2. **Laughter** gives you an emotional boost while reducing stress. Both can stimulate vagal tone, so watch more comedies and try to surround yourself around funny, lighthearted people.

3. **Cold exposure** - Exposing yourself to cold temperatures or going from hot to cold showers can suppress the "fight or flight"

response and promote relaxation. You can start by turning the cold water on for the last 30 seconds of your shower.

4. **Singing, chanting, or humming** a vibrating tone, such as Mmm... This one is very powerful since the vagus nerve is connected to the vocal cords in the back of the throat.

5. **Intermittent fasting** means fasting for a certain number of hours throughout the day. You can start by fasting for 14 hours and eating for 10 or fasting for 16 hours and eating for 8. The vagus nerve oversees digestion and fasting will give your vagus nerve a well needed break.

6. **Consuming probiotics** - You can increase your probiotic intake by incorporating yogurt, kefir milk, sauerkraut, or other fermented foods into your diet.

7. **Omega 3 fatty acids** are excellent for brain health and contribute to a reduction in heart rate, as well as heart rate variability, which are both directly connected to the vagus nerve.

8. **Exercise** contributes to a healthy brain and can reverse cognitive degeneration, which can both be attributed to a strong vagal tone.

9. **Massage**, which includes mostly reflexology or foot massage. You can also massage the right side of your throat.

10. **Vibrating massagers or vibrating platforms** - Ok, now set those naughty thoughts aside and stay with me here. These vibrating machines can reduce stress, encourage relaxation, relieve joint and back pain, improve circulation, build muscles, strengthen bones, boost metabolism, and even drain the lymphatic system. These vibrating platforms are even used for astronauts in outer space to keep them from losing muscle tone and bone density. These vibrations will also exercise your vagus nerve. You can purchase one for under $150 online.

Chapter 6: In a Nutshell

1. There is such a strong connection between the brain and gut, that an issue in the brain is almost always indicative of a problem in the gut. The gut produces 90% of serotonin and 50% of dopamine, and they need the neural pathways to be clear in order to make their way to the brain. Inflammation or any digestive issues can interfere with the production and transportation of these happy chemicals.

2. The microbiome consists of good guys and bad guys. In order to encourage a balanced atmosphere, the good guys need to dominate this relationship. This can be done by incorporating more foods that contain probiotics, while limiting processed foods, sugars, and antibiotics.

3. If you suffer from digestive issues, it would be beneficial to incorporate an elimination diet to help pinpoint the cause, and potentially rid yourself of this sensitivity.

4. The vagus nerve is the longest of all nerves in the body. It has an effect on almost every organ. The vagus nerve is directly connected to the nervous system and anxiety, so strengthening and stimulating vagal tone is necessary in order to get more control of the bossy brain.

Chapter 7: Eliminate and Nourish

Now that we understand the biology of our body a bit more, it's time to focus on eliminating triggers, as well supplying our body with exactly what it needs in order to function properly.

In order to keep your bossy brain in check, you need to have a healthy, well balanced lifestyle that includes 7 - 8 hours of sleep, and plenty of exercise. Your diet should consist of lots of vegetables, fruits, legumes, whole grains, nuts, and lean protein. You should try to avoid any refined foods, such as simple carbohydrates and sugars, which include white breads and white sugars. Refined foods are any foods that have been stripped of bran, fiber, and nutrients.

Also, avoid any mind-altering substances, such as caffeinated beverages, cigarettes, drugs, alcohol, and even excessive amounts of sugar. Did you know that sugar is just as addictive as cocaine? Crazy, right?!

Our bodies require certain nutrients to function properly. This is why I encourage you to go to the doctor to ensure you're not deficient in any essential vitamins and minerals. This is very important! The slightest deficiency can have a significant impact on your mood and brain function. The most important nutrients to check for are B1, B6,

B12, zinc, iron, magnesium, and vitamin D. Once we confirm that you're not nutrient deficient, we can then focus on detoxing, healing, and balancing the body.

Keep the bossy brain in check with these vitamins and minerals

1. B Vitamins

Vitamin B1 is responsible for maintaining blood sugar. Blood sugar levels that are too high or too low can contribute to anxiety.

Vitamin B3 plays a role in serotonin production, which helps with mood and sleep.

Vitamin B5 can help reduce stress by supporting the adrenal glands.

Vitamin B6 plays a role in the production of serotonin and GABA, both of which promote relaxation and elevated mood. Vitamin B6 along with magnesium can also help alleviate PMS symptoms.

Vitamin B12 is the most important B vitamin when it comes to the brain and nervous system. B12 has even been a popular choice for treating depression. Any deficiency can lead to disruptions in the nervous system, cognition, the circulatory system and even anemia. Some symptoms of a deficiency can be fatigue, weakness, numbness, tingling in the hands and feet, confusion, and poor memory. Those at most risk for a deficiency would be vegans, the elderly, and people with a compromised immune system.

   Note: The good thing about taking a vitamin B supplement is that they are water soluble. This means that your body will simply flush out any excess that it doesn't need. Note that B vitamins pack you with energy, so if you're taking too much, it can interfere with the quality of your sleep. As we know, getting enough sleep is super important in order to keep the bossy brain in check. So, I would recommend getting your B levels checked, and monitoring your quality of sleep while taking the supplement.

2. **Magnesium**

Magnesium is an essential mineral that plays many important roles throughout the body. People suffering from anxiety can benefit greatly from taking a magnesium supplement. It reduces inflammation, and helps improve nerve, muscle, and brain function by reducing stress and promoting relaxation. It also plays an important role in nerve impulse, muscle contraction, and heart rhythm, all of which are related to anxiety.

A Magnesium deficiency can result in anxiety, depression, psychosis or other mental and behavioral disturbances. Some symptoms include headache, muscle cramps, irritability, heart palpitations, nervousness, and fatigue. Magnesium deficiencies can be connected to excessive stress, too much calcium consumption, excessive sweating, and not eating enough magnesium rich foods. Stress is a magnesium buzz kill, so those experiencing anxiety and who are chronically stressed are most likely magnesium deficient.

Magnesium is stored in our cells and bones, so a blood test won't be helpful in detecting a deficiency. Try to ensure you're eating magnesium rich foods, which consist of dark leafy greens, avocados, almonds, cashews, lentils, beans, chickpeas, tofu, flaxseed, chia seeds, salmon, bananas, and bone broth. Unfortunately, our soil has been depleted of essential minerals over the years, and our water has been stripped of most of its magnesium. So, if you suffer from anxiety or depression, I recommend taking a magnesium supplement. You can check online to see how much magnesium you should take, based on your age and gender. Do not exceed the recommended daily allowance and exercise caution if you have abnormal kidney function. Getting too much magnesium can cause abnormal heart function. You should also check if magnesium interferes with any medication you may be taking.

Exercise that consists of excessive sweating can drain your body of electrolytes, such as magnesium. When I first started doing Bikram Yoga, I noticed that I would leave the studio feeling anxious. I couldn't figure out why I kept feeling this way, especially since yoga is known to be relaxing. Bikram Yoga is an intense 1.5 hour class that incorporates 105-degree heat, along with 26 postures. I was losing a lot of electrolytes, especially magnesium, by sweating excessively. After each class I felt irritable, jittery, and nervous, which would last for days. It felt like my nervous system was all out of whack, which made me think of magnesium. Finally, I realized that I was losing too many electrolytes by excessively sweating. Now I take a daily magnesium supplement, and make sure I consume foods high in electrolytes after each class. So, if you're someone who sweats excessively during exercise, make sure you're supplementing with magnesium or electrolytes. Electrolytes include sodium, magnesium, chloride, calcium, and potassium. Some foods that are high in electrolytes would be bananas, tomatoes, avocado and coconut water.

3. **Zinc**

Zinc can be found throughout the body but has the highest levels in the hippocampus. It's responsible for healthy nerve transmission, brain function, and can reduce inflammation. It also enhances GABA activity, which is very calming for the brain. Zinc can help maintain normal stress levels, but excessive stress can also strip us of this very important mineral.

A zinc deficiency could contribute to anxiety, depression, ADHD, dementia, bipolar, seizures, aggression, learning impairment, and loss of memory. People at highest risk of a deficiency include vegetarians, women who are pregnant or breastfeeding, people who drink too much alcohol, people with poor diets, the elderly, and those with malabsorption or digestive issues.

Studies have shown that people with anxiety have lower levels of zinc in their body. For this reason, you may want to consider upping your zinc intake. There is a flip side to this, because more is not always better. I would recommend that you focus on eating zinc rich foods, rather than taking a supplement. Eat foods like oysters, red meat, poultry, beans, nuts, and whole grains. Having your zinc levels checked may be beneficial so that you know whether you should take a supplement or not.

4. **Iron**

Iron facilitates the production of hemoglobin in red blood cells, which then carries oxygen throughout the body. People at risk for an iron deficiency are vegetarians, vegans, women who experience heavy periods, anyone who's experienced heavy blood loss in general, the elderly, and those with chronic conditions that lead to loss of red blood cells. Some symptoms of an iron deficiency include exhaustion, fatigue, heart palpitations, cold hands and feet, mood swings, shortness of breath, and poor circulation. When there is a lack of iron circulating throughout the body, there is less oxygen reaching the bodily tissues. A lack of oxygen to the brain can cause mental confusion, impairment, brain fog, and low dopamine production, which can all contribute to anxiety.

5. **Vitamin D3**

Vitamin D3 is so important at every level throughout the body. The body cannot function properly without adequate levels of vitamin D. It's pretty common for most people to be deficient, especially those with limited access to sunlight, vegetarians, people who are overweight, the elderly, and those who don't consume much dairy. Studies have shown that people with anxiety or depression had lower levels of calcidiol, which is a byproduct of vitamin D. There are vitamin D receptors throughout the body, but they are more concentrated in the part of the brain that's linked with depression. It also helps regulate the immune system and facilitates the release of dopamine and serotonin.

Although vitamin D has amazing benefits, it is possible to get too much of it. For this reason, I recommend having your levels checked by your doctor before you start supplementing. You can also increase your intake naturally through eating more fatty fish, egg yolk, mushrooms, tofu, yogurt, and kefir. Getting 15 minutes of sunlight every few days is also a great way to increase your vitamin D levels.

6. **Omega 3 Fatty Acids**

Omega 3 Fatty Acids are so incredibly beneficial to the brain, that if you were to take one vitamin daily, this should be it! It's a healthy polyunsaturated fat that reduces inflammation, improves nerve conduction, improves brain function, and can even help prevent or alleviate symptoms associated with Alzheimer's and dementia. People with depression and anxiety have also shown improvements after taking a fish oil supplement. When you look at countries with the lowest rates of depression, you'll find that Japan has one of the lowest cases, and this could be due to the high intake of fish. Shoot for a fish oil supplement that contains at least 250 mg of DHA + EPA. Within a day or two of taking fish oil, you should be able to notice an improvement in memory and cognition.

While omega 3 fatty acids are excellent for the brain, omega 6 fatty acids are the ones we need to keep in check. These fatty acids are associated with saturated fats, which contributes to inflammation. It's easy to accumulate large amounts of omega 6 in your body, because they come from processed foods, such as meats, soybean, corn, and peanuts. High amounts of omega 6 could cause problems within the body, including inflammation in the brain. Those with mood disorders could possibly have too much omega 6 or too little omega 3. When the brain is inflamed, there is a disruption in the nerve communication and the happy chemicals have a hard time making their way to the brain.

The two omega 3 fatty acids in the brain are DHA and EPA. DHA facilitates normal brain function, while EPA is anti-inflammatory which helps improve the nervous system. These fatty acids can also help alleviate brain fog, help you focus, and improve memory, which can give you a better headspace. Our body does not typically produce omega 3, so we need to make sure we get it through our diet, or by taking supplements. Foods that are high in omega 3 are cold water fish like salmon, sea bass, sardines, and cod. Other foods that contain omega 3's are walnuts, kidney beans, flaxseed, chia seeds, and avocados.

7. **Ginkgo Biloba**

Ginkgo Biloba is known for its brain boosting abilities and helps keep the bossy brain in check. Ginkgo Biloba contains lots of antioxidants to combat oxidative stress. Oxidative stress can contribute to inflammation, tissue damage, cognitive impairment, and mood disorders, so keeping it in check with ginkgo biloba could help reduce added stress, which would help with anxiety. Ginkgo biloba is also known to increase blood flow throughout the body, including the brain, which means there's more oxygen reaching the brain. Therefore, this brain supplement is known to boost antioxidants, reduce inflammation, and increase oxygen to the brain, which would all result in improved brain function.

Bossy Brain Busting Foods

1. **Green tea** contains L-theanine, which is an amino acid that has been shown to produce a calming effect, while stimulating dopamine, GABA, and serotonin. A typical cup of tea contains around 25 mg, but you have to consume around 200 mg in order to reap the benefits. If this is too much for you, consider buying the supplement, rather than bombarding yourself with 8 cups of green tea a day.

2. **Kefir milk, yogurt, or a probiotic supplement** will help increase the good guys in your gut, while keeping the bad guys in check. Read the labels to make sure the sugar content isn't too high, especially with those popular yogurt brands. Sometimes you'll find that there's over 40 grams of sugar in one of those little yogurt cups. Remember that the bad guys feed off of sugar, causing them to grow and take over the good guys. Try adding fruit or stevia instead of sugar. If you choose to start taking a probiotic supplement, try to take it on an empty stomach, so the good guys can do their work more efficiently.

3. **Blueberries** are rich in vitamin C and antioxidants. This can help with oxidative stress, which is when the body tries to detox

itself against free radicals by using antioxidants. Providing your body with extra antioxidants will help combat the oxidative stress. Remember that we want to avoid any stress within our body. You can also incorporate dark leafy greens, fruits and veggies with bright colors, such as beets, carrots, broccoli, and pumpkins.

4. **Apples and cherries** are rich in boron, which is a mineral that can improve your quality of sleep and reduce stress.

5. **Dark leafy greens, avocados, almonds, and dark chocolate** are rich in magnesium. The cocoa is the nutritious part of the dark chocolate, so make sure there is a minimum of 70% cocoa. Also make sure the dark chocolate is low in sugar to avoid feeding the bad guys.

6. **Sesame seeds** are little miracle seeds that you need to incorporate in your diet, like yesterday! These tiny little seeds are packed with magnesium, calcium, iron, thiamin and tryptophan, making them an anxiety busting super seed. These seeds also help with diabetes, blood pressure, cholesterol, digestion, heart health, cancer prevention, DNA damage, anemia, liver function, bone health, eye health, arthritis, skin and hair. Sesame seeds can even help prevent gray hair and balding, as well as reverse it. Can you believe that? Ok, so I know you're thinking, "how the heck am I going to incorporate enough sesame seeds in my diet to see these benefits?" So, what I do is I usually buy 5 pounds of black sesame seeds online, and then put 1 tablespoon in my smoothie every morning. You won't even notice the taste at all, and this is a great way of adding it to your daily routine. You can also sprinkle it over your salads or even take it as a supplement.

7. **Bacopa Monnieri** is an herb commonly used in Ayurvedic medicine, which has been known to boost brain function and memory. Bacopa contains bacosides, which protect the brain from oxidative stress by facilitating antioxidants to fight free radicals. It also stimulates the hippocampus, which is the portion of your brain responsible for memory. Bacopa benefits may also include a reduction in stress, anxiety, inflammation, and blood

pressure. The decreased inflammation and regulated blood pressure can clear the neural pathways within the brain, which can boost cognition.

This is Your Brain on Sugar

Remember that drug campaign from the late 80's? The advertisement showed a visual of a frying egg along with the slogan saying, "This is your brain on drugs." Well, I feel like there should be another campaign on sugar, saying "This is your brain on sugar." I'd imagine the visual would be something like fireworks going off in a house, because that's what your brain cells look like after a sugar binge. This erratic activity results in brain rush, racing thoughts, confusion, lack of focus, and brain fog. Not to mention, sugar can be just as addicting as drugs. When you consume sugar, you first experience a spike in blood sugar, then a spike in insulin, followed by a crash shortly afterward, which leaves you wanting more. Sugar also releases large amounts of dopamine, which is why you get a sense of pleasure when you eat it. This constant release of dopamine keeps you addicted, while draining your reserves.

You can crave sugar for days after you cut it out of your diet, and you might even experience withdrawal symptoms. So yes, I'd consider sugar a drug, because it absolutely alters brain function, and is extremely addicting. Consuming excessive amounts of sugar can also promote inflammation and block the absorption of calcium and magnesium. Inflammation makes it harder for your brain cells to function and communicate normally, while calcium and magnesium are necessary to promote relaxation, and good nerve health. Also, those with yeast overgrowth in their digestive tract can literally create a brewery in their body after a sugar binge. Unfortunately, you may feel like you skipped the fun night of partying and went straight to the hangover. Yeast feeds on sugar, which creates alcohol as a byproduct, and this is what leads to a sugar hangover.

I get that giving up sugar is not easy, but it would be best to avoid all simple sugars, such as white sugar, white bread, candy, and soda. The problem with simple sugars is that they are absorbed quickly in the blood, which is what causes the hyperactivity in your brain. When you eat more complex sugars, such as fruit or oatmeal, they have more nutrients and fiber in them, slowing down absorption, so that you don't get that brain rush.

Aspartame - Not So Sweet After All

Now that you're trying to limit your sugar, don't run to aspartame. Aspartame is a commonly used sugar substitute in sugar free candy, diet soda, and sugar free gum. This sugar alternative can cause all kinds of mental issues, such as anxiety, depression, bipolar, Alzheimer's, dementia, and memory impairment. Studies even found that long term use can actually lead to brain tumors. The FDA actually banned this chemical twice, but it somehow weaseled its way back into our food through a shady political scandal when Ronald Reagan was in office.

Aspartame consists of 3 chemicals known as aspartic acid, phenylalanine, and methanol. When aspartame is consumed, it blocks tryptophan production, while increasing levels of phenylalanine. Tryptophan is essential in creating serotonin, while phenylalanine inhibits the release of serotonin and dopamine. These are happy chemicals that protect us from mood disorders, and now they are being blocked by the chemicals produced by aspartame. It also acts as a chemical stressor, causing an increase in free radicals in the body, which can contribute to oxidative stress. We are trying to limit stress in the body, not encourage it. I would recommend checking your food labels to avoid this sweetener. You can substitute sugar with Stevia or Xylitol, which are both natural sweeteners.

The Keto Diet

The keto diet is most popularly known for its benefits related to weight loss. Most people don't know that it can have significant improvements on brain function as well. Versions of the keto diet were actually developed in the early 1900's to help cure epilepsy in children. They found that ketones led to less epileptic seizures, and therefore were able to alter brain function. The keto diet can also help with Alzheimer's, dementia, anxiety, autism, bipolar, ADHD and all kinds of other neurological disorders. It can also improve cognition, memory, clarity, alertness, and focus.

The keto diet is rich in healthy fats, while limiting carbohydrates and sugars. Normally our body runs on glucose as its main source of fuel. Carbohydrates are converted to glucose by the liver and sent out to the rest of the body as fuel. Any excess glucose is converted to glycogen and stored for future energy consumption. When the body is starved of glucose, the liver uses ketones, which is an alternative source of fuel. The body uses fatty acids from foods or from our body fat to create ketones. This is why people burn fat so easily on the keto diet. The body is burning fat for energy, rather than carbohydrates. Ketones also act as a super fuel for the brain. They require less oxygen than glucose, which makes utilizing fuel more efficient. This means more oxygen for the brain. It also releases less byproduct in the process, so your body doesn't have to use extra energy to clean it up.

When glucose is used by the brain, it releases a byproduct called glutamate. When kept in check, glutamate plays a crucial role in memory and learning. However, excessive amounts of glutamate can contribute to over excited nerve cells, which can lead to cellular damage or cell death. This can have a negative impact on the nervous system, contributing to neurological diseases. It can also contribute to brain fog, insomnia, anxiety, and lack of focus. Alternatively, when the body uses ketones, it's able to convert glutamate into glutamine, which is responsible for the creation of GABA. GABA is able to balance out glutamate, and is known for its anti-anxiety, anti-stress, and calming effect. Both neurotransmitters are vital to support a healthy well balanced nervous system, so the idea here is to have both glutamate and GABA live in harmony together. If you are an anxious person, you most likely suffer from high glutamate and low GABA levels, so you can most likely benefit from adopting a low carb diet like the keto diet.

However, there's one last thing to consider. A strict keto diet can possibly decrease your serotonin levels. You can boost serotonin by exercising, as well as eating more salmon, turkey, nuts, and seeds. If you find your anxiety, depression, or insomnia increasing with a strict keto diet, it would be good to increase your carb intake to bring your levels back into balance. Try to find the perfect balance by easing your way into the diet. I would suggest gradually working your carb intake down, rather than just cutting them out completely all at once. This way you can adjust your diet as necessary.

Now going back to glucose vs. ketones for energy production. Ketones are a more efficient means of energy production for the body. They are known to increase mitochondria, which is responsible for producing cellular energy. Less oxygen is needed to produce energy, which means there's more oxygen retained in your body. Your body can now spend this extra energy on healing and regenerating itself. When your brain is lacking oxygen, it can become stressed, and impair cognition, leaving you more vulnerable to your bossy brain. Increased oxygen to the brain would promote clarity, focus, and relaxation, which would enable you to keep your bossy brain in check. This is exactly what people with anxiety need, more oxygen going to their brain, which we'll explore in the next section. Studies have shown that someone in ketosis can hold their breath longer than someone not experiencing ketosis. This might be due to the fact that ketosis reduces the amount of carbon dioxide in the blood. Oxygen is needed to expel carbon dioxide, so less oxygen would be necessary to get the job done. As a result, ketosis leaves more oxygen for the brain, which is what someone with anxiety needs.

The keto diet can also help stabilize blood sugar levels. Constantly eating foods high in sugar and carbohydrates cause your body to keep pumping insulin, resulting in fluctuating blood sugar. When you eat simple carbohydrates, you experience a sharp increase in blood sugar, followed by a sharp decrease. Your levels are usually not stable throughout the day. When you're super hungry, you can experience sharp reductions in blood sugar, which causes your brain to panic, thinking it's going to starve. This is what contributes to that feeling of anxiousness when you're hungry. Since ketones are metabolized more efficiently than glucose, your body is able to fuel itself quicker, leaving less time for the brain to panic. Your brain also knows that it can now use these fat storages for energy, instead of glucose, so there's no longer a need to panic in case of a food famine. You can also avoid those racing thoughts that are associated with a sugar high, since you're no longer eating sugars.

You can also expect a reduction in inflammation by eliminating sugars, processed foods, processed grains, starchy vegetables and other unhealthy fats and carbohydrates. Instead, you'll be eating healthy anti-inflammatory foods rich in polyunsaturated fats, such as eggs, avocados, olive oil, coconut oil, fatty fish, kale, cauliflower, and broccoli.

So, by incorporating a keto diet, you can experience increased oxygen, increased relaxation, improvements in focus, mental clarity, cognition, increased energy, more stable blood sugar levels, and a reduction in inflammation. It can also help protect you against degenerative diseases and other mental health challenges. Why wouldn't you want to do this diet, right? Yeah, I get it. Easier said than done. But for those of you interested to give it a try, here's how you can do it.

Gradually reduce your carbohydrate count, while simultaneously incorporating more healthy fats, and low carb vegetables. One thing to note is that a lot of people have this idea that the keto diet consists of mostly meat, which is not the case at all. This diet should consist of 20% protein, 75% fat, and 5% carbohydrates.

Here's a snapshot of what your diet should look like:

Protein 20%
Chicken, eggs, turkey, salmon, shrimp, and bacon

Fat 75%
Avocado, walnuts, hazelnuts, almonds, coconut oil, olive oil, butter, MCT oil, yogurt, kefir, cheese, and nut milks, such as almond milk, coconut milk, and macadamia nut milk

Carbohydrates 5% (<50 grams per day)

Cauliflower, zucchini, kale, spaghetti squash, butternut squash, blueberries, raspberries, and strawberries.

Sticking to this strict diet of limited carbs and sugar can be very challenging, but there are things you can do to make it more exciting. You can create recipes using stevia, which is an all-natural plant-based sugar substitute, as well as inulin, which is a healthy prebiotic fiber that probiotics feed off of. Strawberries, blackberries and raspberries are acceptable in keto, but just don't overdo it.

I'd like to outline a few risks that can be associated with keto, so please talk to your doctor if you have any pre-existing conditions or are taking any medications.

Here are some things to take into consideration:

1. **Kidney stress and kidney stones** - People with kidney disease are usually advised to reduce their animal protein consumption. Therefore, if you have any kidney related issues, you should avoid eating red meats while on keto.

2. **Diabetes and low blood sugar** - Those with type 1 and type 2 diabetes should proceed with caution before beginning a keto diet. Although keto can help manage your blood sugar levels, there's still the risk of hypoglycemia, which is a dangerous drop in blood sugar.

3. **Dehydration and a reduction in electrolytes** - When the body uses fat instead of carbs for fuel, it produces ketones, which are expelled through urine. Through this process, your body releases retained water and electrolytes to aid in the elimination. Therefore, you should drink plenty of water and consider supplementing with electrolytes while on the diet.

4. **Decreased potassium levels** - This decrease can be due to your reduction in fruit, whole grains, and starchy vegetables. You should supplement your potassium through other low carb foods,

such as almonds, avocado, spinach, salmon, flaxseed, and chia seeds.

5. **Decreased sodium** - Ketosis releases less insulin, which results in your kidneys excreting more sodium. Make sure to add more sodium to your diet, especially if you're sweating a lot during your workouts. You can simply add a pinch of pink Himalayan salt to your cup of water each day.

6. **High cholesterol and heart disease** can be a result of the keto diet if you consume too much unhealthy saturated fats, especially trans fats, which are also known as hydrogenated oils. You should focus on healthy plant based unsaturated fats, such as avocados, olive oil, nuts, seeds, cacao, and dark chocolate. These healthy fats will actually help you fight high cholesterol and heart disease, rather than increase it.

I get that this diet can be very challenging to stick to. Just know that even putting some effort into adopting a low carb diet can provide benefits to your mental health. Just focus on limiting your carbs, sugar, and unhealthy fats, while increasing your veggies, healthy grains, nuts, seeds and healthy fats. This alone should be enough for you to see a difference in cognition, clarity, and focus.

Oxygen Therapy

We talked about how increased oxygen levels can help keep your bossy brain in check, so let's explore this concept a little further.

Mild forms of hypoxia or low blood oxygen levels can contribute to depression, anxiety, and other cognitive issues. Low oxygen levels can be attributed to anemia, asthma, chronic obstructive pulmonary disease (COPD), deviated nasal septum, sinusitis, nasal polyps, sinus allergies, sleep apnea, high altitude, poor circulation, low blood pressure, heart disease, chronic inflammation, and shallow breathing as a result of stress. If you have any of these conditions, consider whether this can be contributing to your anxiety.

Maintaining normal oxygen levels are vital in keeping the brain healthy and functioning properly, so it would be beneficial to have your blood oxygen levels checked.

How to Test Blood Oxygen Levels:

1. **Pulse oximeter** which is a device that clips to the tip of your finger, and usually sells for less than $20. It can measure the amount of oxygen in your hemoglobin. Results above 99% are optimal, while anything below 90% indicates low oxygen levels.

2. **Blood pressure monitor** which is a device that wraps around your arm, putting pressure for a few minutes or so. This can usually be purchased for under $50. Normal blood pressure would be between 90 - 120 / 60 - 80. High blood pressure indicates thicker blood, which is harder to move throughout the body, while low blood pressure would indicate that the blood is not flowing fast enough. Both scenarios would mean that there is a lack of blood flow reaching the brain, indicating low body oxygen.

3. **Blood tests** such as complete blood count, iron, and ferritin levels. Red blood cells carry hemoglobin, which carries oxygen, and the more, the merrier for these oxygen transporters. Low levels of red blood cells, and hemoglobin would indicate an Iron deficiency, which means there's less oxygen in the blood. Ferritins are little iron reserves, which should be tested as well.

Here are signs of low oxygen levels:

- Brain fog or mental confusion
- Headache
- Shortness of breath
- Restlessness
- Heaving or rapid breathing
- Shallow breathing
- Increased heart rate

- Heart palpitations
- Cold hands or feet
- Experiencing a euphoric feeling
- Tingling in the hands or feet
- Arms or legs falling asleep often
- Changes in vision, such as tunnel vision
- Bluish purple lips

How to Increase Oxygen Levels:

1. **Sunlight** boosts circulation and stimulates the production of red blood cells responsible for creating oxygen in the blood.

2. **Quitting smoking** can make a huge improvement in increasing oxygen levels. Smoking constricts the blood, making it harder to flow throughout the body, while replacing oxygen with carbon monoxide.

3. **Yoga** increases blood circulation and promotes relaxation, which can help increase oxygen consumption, while making it flow easily throughout the body.

4. **Abdominal breathing** increases oxygen consumption and promotes relaxation.

5. **Aerobic exercise** increases breath rate, which means you consume and absorb more oxygen.

6. **Open the windows** to help circulate old stale air for fresh oxygenating air within your home.

7. **Fill your home with oxygen producing plants** such as snake plants, money plants, aloe vera, peace lily, and pathos.

Breathing Exercises for Anxiety, Stress Reduction, Relaxation, Brain Health, and Energy:

There are many benefits that can come out of practicing breathing exercises. A higher blood oxygen level can increase cognition, boost energy, promote healing, and even raise athletic and mental peak performance. Diaphragmatic breathing promotes relaxation, which can help reduce stress and anxiety.

Maintaining normal oxygen levels is vital in keeping the brain healthy and functioning properly. Breathing brings oxygen into the body, while exhaling releases carbon dioxide. If there is not enough oxygen coming into the body, then the body is unable to efficiently release carbon dioxide. A lack of oxygen, as well as elevated carbon dioxide levels can mimic symptoms of anxiety, thereby increasing anxiety, stress, and the likelihood of panic attacks.

Two Types of Breathing Styles:

1. **Shallow breathing or vertical breathing** involves raising the shoulders and upper torso vertically while taking an inhale and releasing them upon exhale. The problem with this type of breathing is that the only part of the lungs being utilized is the smaller upper portion. This deprives the body of the oxygen it needs to function at its fullest potential. It also makes it harder for the body to exhale and eliminate carbon dioxide. This type of breathing is usually a result of stress and anxiety. It has unfortunately turned into the most common form of modern-day breathing.

2. **Diaphragmatic breathing, belly breathing, or horizontal breathin**g involves the abdomen expanding out upon inhale and deflating upon exhale. The shoulders and upper chest area should remain still during breathing. Diaphragmatic breathing allows your body to get an adequate amount of oxygen, while eliminating carbon dioxide efficiently. This is how nature intended us to breath.

Determine Your Default Breathing Style:

You can determine what style of breathing your body defaults to by doing this test. Lay on the floor and put one hand over your upper chest area and one hand on your abdomen. Start by breathing how you normally would. Notice which part of your torso is lifting as you inhale and lowering as you exhale. Your shoulders and upper chest should not move, only your lower chest and abdominal area. If your abdomen rises and falls during normal breathing, then you default to diaphragmatic breathing, and you are breathing correctly. You can practice this same exercise while standing to make sure you're not shoulder breathing as well. You can tell if you're shallow breathing if your shoulders rise up as you inhale.

Breathing Exercises:

You can rewire your lungs to breathe correctly by practicing these breathing exercises for 5 - 10 minutes a day and being mindful of the way you are breathing throughout the day. You can practice these exercises before bed to promote relaxation, or in the morning to feel more focused and alert.

1. **Diaphragmatic breathing** - Lay down on a flat comfortable surface. Put one hand over your upper chest and the other hand over your abdomen. Take long, deep, slow breaths and make sure that your abdomen is pushing outward toward your hand, while your upper chest remains still. Exhale your breath slowly through pursed lips. You can purse your lips as if you're blowing a kiss but leaving a small hole to exhale the air through slowly. This is the best breathing exercise for anxiety, as it promotes a deep sense of relaxation.

2. **Engage the pelvic muscles during exhale** - The diaphragm and the pelvic muscles are connected and work together to help you exhale as much air as possible. Start by taking in a deep abdominal breath. Make sure your abdomen and pelvic floor expand during your inhale. As you exhale, squeeze the lower abdominal muscles and contract the pelvic floor.

3. **4-7-8 breathing** involves inhaling through your nose for a count of 4, holding your breath for a count of 7, and exhaling through your mouth for a count of 8. This is an excellent breathing technique for promoting sleepiness.

4. **Alternate Nostril Breathing** - Start by sitting in a comfortable seated position. Rest your hands on your knees, palms facing up. Take your right hand and rest your pointy finger and index finger in between your eyebrows. Close the right nostril with your right thumb and take a breath through your left nostril. Hold the breath and close the left nostril with your right ring finger, while releasing your right thumb to exhale through your right nostril. Repeat this breathing exercise for 10 - 20 breaths or until you feel relaxed.

Hyperbaric Oxygen Therapy

Ok, I know this sounds like an intense treatment, but people are seeing some great benefits by using this type of therapy. Hyperbaric Oxygen Therapy is a treatment that exposes the patient to oxygen in a pressurized environment, which allows the lungs to take in 3 x more oxygen than normal. It works by putting the body in a pressurized state which decreases the size of oxygen molecules so that they are able to dissolve in blood plasma and travel throughout the body as needed in order to promote healing.

The treatment consists of multiple sessions at a clinic, or a hyperbaric chamber can be rented out, so that the sessions can be done at home. This groundbreaking therapy can help recovery from concussions, brain or bodily injuries, mental health conditions and cognitive issues. This type of therapy is already successfully treating people with PTSD, and they are currently working on incorporating this therapy for other types of mental health challenges.

It's worth looking into this type of therapy, especially if there's a possibility that your anxiety is related to some type of injury or deficiency that's causing a lack of oxygen.

Inflammation - The Inflamed Brain

There is growing research that suggests that there may be a correlation between inflammation and depression. Inflammation is the immune system's first line of defense when battling foreign invaders, such as bacteria, viruses, parasites, fungus, disease, and injury. It can be a lifesaving response that our body deploys. However, excessive and continuous inflammation can be damaging as well. Inflammation blocks the neural pathways making it harder to send signals so that the brain can function properly. This blockage also interferes with the production and transportation of the happy chemicals to the brain. There are many other things that contribute to inflammation, such as lifestyle, stress, and the foods we eat. Having long term inflammation in our body can wreak havoc throughout our system, especially in our brains.

Consider some of the happiest and healthiest tribes in the world, which are the Hunza people of Northern Pakistan and the Abkhazia people of the Northeast Coast of the Black Sea. Their diet and way of living are conducive to an anti-inflammatory lifestyle. They mostly eat raw plant-based foods, such as fruits, veggies, whole grains, nuts, and seeds, while not consuming any refined oils, flour, or sugar. They are extremely active throughout the day, and embrace a simple lifestyle, which means they typically have less stress than most other people in the world. This goes to show you that there's potentially a strong correlation between inflammation and anxiety or depression.

Cytokines present in the blood are usually an indication of inflammation. These levels tend to be higher in those with anxiety and depression. Cytokines are a protein that communicate inflammatory signals throughout the body, so an excessive amount would indicate inflammation. Cytokines block oxygen from reaching the tissues from the capillaries, which results in lower oxygen levels. Maintaining healthy oxygen levels is vital for optimal brain function, so any imbalance can contribute to cognitive impairment.

The vagus nerve that we learned about earlier is known to block inflammation. The vagus nerve has senses all throughout the body, and when it senses the presence of cytokines or other inflammation markers, it tells the brain to release anti-inflammatory neurotransmitters that regulate the body's immune response. More of a reason to strengthen this important nerve.

110

There have been very few studies done on the correlation between inflammation and anxiety, but it's known that people with PTSD have high levels of inflammation. PTSD and panic attacks cause stress to the body, which in turn contributes to inflammation. Each panic attack causes stress, and stress causes inflammation, which then causes more anxiety. This can keep anxiety and inflammation in a perpetual ongoing cycle.

The two types of inflammation are acute and chronic. Acute inflammation usually arises as a result of injury or infection. Chronic inflammation is usually associated with diseases, such as arthritis, allergies, diabetes, Crohn's disease, asthma, and heart disease.

Symptoms of acute inflammation:

- Pain when the affected area is touched
- Continuous pain in the same area
- Loss of function mostly due to swelling, such as the inability to move joints as a result of arthritis
- Swelling as a result of blood flow, and fluid build up
- Heat or redness as a result of increased blood flow to the affected area

Symptoms of chronic inflammation:

- Chronic fatigue, nausea, and insomnia
- Digestive disorders that include bloating, diarrhea, constipation, and acid reflux
- Depression, anxiety, and other mood disorders
- Recurring inflections, such as sinus infections, UTI, yeast infections, or candida

What causes inflammation:

1. **Stress and oxidative stress** cause our body to pump out stress hormones, which are actually anti-inflammatory. However,

chronic stress deteriorates the stress hormone's ability to keep inflammation in check, which results in excessive inflammation down the line.

2. **Smoking** triggers white blood cells called neutrophils, which can lead to inflammation. Smoking is also damaging to the lungs, and causes oxidative stress, which can also lead to inflammation.

3. **Insomnia** - We produce inflammatory markers called cytokine during our sleep. Sleep deprivation would deprive the body of this important anti-inflammatory and pro-inflammatory chemical. This means inflammation would fail to protect us when needed or it could easily get out of control due to the lack of cytokines to help keep it in check.

4. **Old age** which could be a result of accumulated free radicals, body fat, and deterioration of the brain and body overtime.

5. **Obesity or being overweight** causes an inflammatory response because our immune system views it as a threat. This can become especially dangerous when inflammation occurs within the arterial walls where the fat is located. This constricts blood flow even more, which can lead to problems related to the brain and heart.

6. **Poor eating habits** that include excessive red or processed meat, sugar, processed foods, refined carbohydrates, fried foods, preservatives, additives, and alcohol. Dairy and gluten can also cause inflammation because it has become harder to digest due to its overuse in our food over the years. You can find gluten and dairy as an ingredient in a majority of processed foods. Overexposure to anything can lead to allergies and intolerances, which contributes to inflammation.

7. **Low sex hormones** can contribute to inflammation due to the decrease in anti-inflammatory testosterone and estrogen. Women who are going through menopause may experience higher levels of inflammation. Likewise, men who experience low sex drive,

loss of body hair, fatigue, or loss of muscle mass may have unusually low levels of testosterone, resulting in excessive inflammation.

How to reduce inflammation:

1. Eat more anti-inflammatory foods such as fatty fish containing omega 3's, dark leafy greens, ginger, turmeric, walnuts, almonds, flaxseed, chia seeds, organic berries, cruciferous veggies (broccoli, kale, etc.), avocados, organic green tea, organic grapes, mushrooms, bell peppers, tomatoes, and cherries.

2. Eat less inflammatory foods such as red or processed meat, sugar, processed foods, refined carbohydrates, fried foods, preservatives, additives, and alcohol.

3. Exercise at least 3 days per week to increase blood flow and reduce fat cells that are causing inflammation.

4. Reduce stress and anxiety through exercise, yoga, meditation, or other stress reducing techniques.

5. Heal chronic infections such as recurring UTI, candida, IBS, digestive issues, and food intolerances.

6. Oxygen therapy can speed up healing of an injury that could be blocking oxygen from reaching the brain.

Anti-Inflammatory Supplements

- Curcumin
- Ginger
- Bacopa Monnieri
- Fish oil
- Resveratrol
- Bromelain
- Spirulina

- Cat's claw
- Vitamin E
- Garlic
- Cayenne pepper
- Zinc

As with any new supplements, make sure to do your research to ensure you're taking the right dosage, and that there are no negative interactions with any medications you might be taking. Vitamin E and Zinc can have negative effects if taken in excess. There are blood tests the doctor can give you to let you know if you are deficient.

These Heavy Metal Can be Hurting Your Brain

Heavy metal exposure to mercury, aluminum, and lead can contribute to anxiety, depression, and other cognitive issues. An accumulation of these heavy metals can lead to harmful effects on the nervous system and digestive tract. Heavy metals can damage or kill neurons, inhibit serotonin, dopamine, and norepinephrine production, as well as impair digestion. They can also increase the risk associated with Alzheimer's, dementia, autism, and ADHD. Some symptoms of excessive heavy metal exposure can be fatigue, irritability, mood disorders, poor concentration, brain fog, headaches, and insomnia.

I know you're probably thinking, "How the heck would I be exposed to these heavy metals?" But the truth is, exposure is a lot more common than you may think. And the problem with continuous exposure, even at low levels, is that you accumulate a lot of these heavy metals in your brain, bones, cells, and tissues. The most effective way of detoxing these heavy metals is through chelating with cilantro or chlorella. What these supplements will do is bind to the heavy metals and escort them out of your body. Mercury exposure is the most common of the 3 and most closely linked to brain health, so let's start with that.

Mercury

Mercury can make its way into our bodies through consuming larger and longer living fish, such as fresh tuna and swordfish. If you love your fish, then you should eat smaller, shorter living fish like salmon, shrimp, cod, and catfish. Farmed fish does have less mercury than wild fish, although I'm not a big fan. Those farmed fish contain antibiotics, are higher in inflammatory omega 6, contain PCBs, and live in unhealthy overpopulated conditions.

Another form of exposure is through drinking water. It makes its way into our drinking water through runoff from landfill and agriculture. The acceptable amount of mercury in our drinking water is now regulated by the EPA, but they still allow small amounts to be present. If you're interested in removing mercury from your water, there are systems that can do that, such as reverse osmosis systems installed under your sink or mercury removing water filters.

People who've worked in the dental industry and those who have amalgam fillings, may have excessive mercury exposure. The buildup is a result of mercury vapor released by cavities filled with amalgam. Dentists and dental staff can be exposed while filling a patient's cavities. In the past, studies have shown that dentists may have the highest suicidal rates out of all health professions. This could be attributed to mercury toxicity and how it affects mental health. People who have amalgam fillings in their mouth will have a lifetime exposure to mercury vapor. At normal temperatures, the mercury lays dormant. However, every time it's heated up through drinking tea, coffee or hot soups, it releases vapors, which are then absorbed by the body.

Mercury stores itself in the fatty tissues of the body, especially in the brain. This is what makes testing for mercury toxicity complicated, because the amount of mercury in your body will not be accurately reflected in a blood test. The reason for this is that the mercury is not running through your blood, it's stored in your cells and tissues. Mercury is slowly released through urine, feces, breathing, and breast milk over time. Some individuals aren't able to eliminate mercury from their body as quickly, which can result in an increased risk of toxicity.

If you'd like to test your mercury levels, know that testing your blood, urine, or hair will not give you an accurate reading. You would need to have a trained physician give you a medication with sulfur molecules, which binds to the mercury and then eliminates it through the urine. Based on the levels in your urine, the doctor can tell how much mercury is stored in your body.

Yeah, who wants to do all that, right? You may just want to consider having your amalgam cavity fillings replaced with composite and avoid fish that contain high levels of mercury. Don't get freaked out by replacing your fillings, they should be replaced every 10 years or so anyways. You can also try chelating mercury naturally using cilantro and chlorella, which can help remove 91% of mercury within 45 days. Try to take these on an empty stomach for optimal effectiveness.

Root Canal

Most of the people working in the dental industry don't believe that mercury or root canals are harmful to your health. There's a lot of money involved in this industry, especially related to these procedures. Therefore, the American Dental Association has campaigned against these claims and have posted many articles, videos, and information out there contradicting what I am telling you. This is why you will find claims from both sides when doing your research and it may leave you feeling indifferent or confused. I just want to make you aware of some of the potential dangers known to be associated with these procedures so you can make an informed decision on how you want to handle it.

Root Canals are a procedure used as a way to save a tooth that is severely decayed or infected. It involves disconnecting the tooth from its nerve supply, blood supply and the lymphatic system. In a healthy tooth, your blood supply and lymph system work together regularly to eliminate harmful bacteria and viruses. However, in a root canaled tooth, there is no nerve supply, which means there is no way for you to feel the pain from an infected tooth. By the time you feel the pain,

116

the little critters have already taken over the dead tooth and spread to other locations. And yes, that's what a root canal is, "a dead tooth." Our teeth are alive, just like anything else in our body.

So now these little critters accumulate, making their way to the roots and surrounding bones. At this point, the toxic bacteria makes its way into the body through the blood and lymphatic system. This can cause problems with the heart, brain, and digestive tract. In addition, this bacterial overgrowth can stress out the immune system, since it will be on overdrive trying to control the overload. And to make things even worse, the root canaled tooth has mercury surrounding it.

Ok, sorry for causing you more stress. I know you're probably wondering how the heck you're going to get this dead tooth out of your mouth. Obviously, you most likely don't want to run to the dentist to have them pull out all your root canaled teeth. So, I would suggest keeping the surrounding area extremely clean at all times. If you have any of the symptoms listed below, I would suggest having x-rays or a dental CT scan done to make sure there's no infection. If the root canaled tooth is infected, I would consider removing it, since the tooth is obviously prone to bacterial accumulation, and it will most likely keep happening.

<u>Here are some signs and symptoms of an infected root canal</u>:

- Pain or discomfort especially when eating or putting pressure on the tooth
- Sensitivity to extreme temperatures
- Pus discharge
- Red, warm, swollen gums or tenderness of the surrounding tissues
- Lump growing on the gums
- Swollen lymph nodes under the jaw or neck
- Tooth darkening
- Bad breath or a bad taste in your mouth

Next time your dentist recommends getting a root canal, I would suggest getting a second opinion from a reputable dentist. I had a dentist tell me that I needed a root canal over 10 years ago, which I never ended up getting, and my tooth is perfectly fine. If your second opinion agrees that you should get a root canal, then I would suggest having the tooth extracted if it's a possibility. Overall, your best plan of action should be to keep your teeth in optimal health in order to avoid a root canal scenario in the first place.

Aluminum

Another toxic metal we're commonly exposed to is aluminum. Not only can aluminum contribute to nerve and cognitive dysfunction, but it can also contribute to breast cancer. Most people are not aware that commonly used deodorant brands contain aluminum, which is putting them at risk. This toxic heavy metal is applied directly on the armpits, which can easily make its way to the surrounding breast tissue. There are certain brands that do not contain aluminum, so I would suggest switching your deodorant as soon as possible. Aluminum may also be linked to Alzheimer's and dementia, due to high levels detected in their body.

Aluminum can also make its way into the body through canned foods, aluminum foil, aluminum cookware, aerosol products, and processed foods, so try to minimize the use of these products as much as possible. If you use canned food, make sure to remove the food from the can as quickly as possible. The reason is that the aluminum becomes more potent when exposed to oxygen. Aluminum cookware can be replaced with safer alternatives, such as stainless steel, cast iron, or ceramic cookware.

Unfortunately, aluminum can make its way into our bodies through less obvious or unavoidable ways, such as through drinking water, vegetables, fruits, meat, baking ingredients, medications, vaccines, and even dialysis.

Aluminum can be found in the human brain, bones, feces, urine, and blood; however, most doctors will not offer these tests, especially since aluminum in the bones or brain would require a biopsy. It would be more beneficial to limit your exposure as much as possible and begin a heavy metal detox.

Lead

Lead is highly toxic, but potential exposure is not as common as mercury and aluminum. Those at most risk are children who put toys in their mouth that contain lead. Parents should always read toy labels to make sure they are lead free. Houses painted before the 1950's are also known to contain lead. It's not possible to remove the lead from these houses, so the walls must be painted over. Other means of exposure consist of art supplies, under-fired pottery that is usually imported from other countries, canned foods, and old plumbing fixtures which slowly release lead into household water.

Lead is highly toxic, and it should be avoided at all costs. In excessive amounts, it can cause anemia, impaired nervous system, and brain damage. In moderate amounts, it can contribute to anxiety, depression, and many other mood disorders.

Heavy Metal Detox

A lot of the time, heavy metal exposure is unavoidable, so everyone should consider doing a heavy metal detox every so often. You can start by adding at least one of the following to your daily routine. Try to consume these on an empty stomach for the most effectiveness.

- Chelating with cilantro, garlic, or parsley
- Spirulina and chlorella supplements
- Chia and flaxseed
- Coconut oil
- Milk thistle
- Wheatgrass or barley juice

You can accelerate the elimination of these heavy metals by drinking plenty of water, as well as sweating through exercise or sauna. Make sure to bathe immediately after sweating, so the metals don't get reabsorbed in the body. If you're using a sauna, I recommend taking showers in between your session and re-entering the sauna a few times. This way you are constantly removing the heavy metals as they are being excreted.

By using these elimination techniques, you can alleviate some of the symptoms that are associated with a heavy metal detox. Some symptoms include headache, bloating, nausea, vomiting, rashes, low energy, metallic taste in the mouth, brain fog, and insomnia. Heavy metals are stored in the bones, brain, and fat cells, which are released during detox. This creates an overflow of metals in the bloodstream, liver, and kidneys, which is what causes these symptoms. If you do experience any of these symptoms, they should subside within a week or two.

Wheatgrass - A Healing Superfood

I found wheatgrass shots to be very helpful when I first did my heavy metal detox. I knew it was working because I experienced headaches and brain fog for 2 weeks once I started taking it. Once the symptoms went away, I felt great! I was thinking clearer, able to focus, full of energy, and my digestion improved. I have been juicing my own wheatgrass for over 10 years now and will continue doing it for the rest of my life. It's a commitment that takes time, but you will have so much energy from the wheatgrass that you won't mind spending it on maintaining your regimen.

Wheatgrass is an amazing superfood that contains 17 amino acids essential for protein creation. It's packed with chlorophyll, contains 92 minerals required by the human body, iron, calcium, magnesium, vitamin A, B, C, E, K, and digestive enzymes. It can eliminate toxins, assist in digestion, increase metabolism, lower cholesterol, boost immunity, boost energy, lower blood pressure, improve cognition, help with arthritis, and is super alkalizing. It may even kill cancer cells. Just to put this into perspective, a 1 oz shot of wheatgrass is equivalent to 2 pounds of spinach. Ok, this list goes on and on and the benefits are awesome. Why would anyone not want to drink this magical juice? Well, I get it. Probably because most people have seen the price tag at the juice store, which usually runs around $4 per shot. What if I told you that you can grow and juice your own wheatgrass at home? Well, you can and here's how you do it.

All you need is a few appetizers over ice trays, some organic non-GMO wheatgrass seeds, a sprouting jar with a screen lid, a slow juicer that can process wheatgrass, a spray bottle, and some dedication.

Growing Your Wheatgrass

1. Measure about ¾ a cup of wheatgrass seeds.

2. Soak the wheatgrass seeds in the sprouting jar for 8 - 12 hours. Make sure to place the jar in indirect sunlight.

3. Empty the water from the sprouting jar leaving the seeds moist, but not soaking in the water.

4. Rinse the seeds morning and night for a few days.

5. Once the wheatgrass has roots that are about 1/4 inch thick, it's time for potting.

6. Fill the appetizers over ice trays with water up until the bottom of the open grooves. If your wheatgrass seeds are touching the water, then you've added too much. The seeds should be right above the water line, so that their roots can make their way down.

7. Now spray your wheatgrass seeds with a bit of water. The key is to keep your seeds moist, but not drenched. I usually lightly spray the seeds every morning until the green grass starts growing. Then I just let it do its thing. (Optional: 1) You can add a teaspoon of baking soda to your spray bottle if you start seeing mold on your seeds. (Optional: 2) You can add 1 tablespoon of kelp liquid to your spray bottle to give your wheatgrass an extra boost.

8. Once your wheatgrass is about 5 inches tall, you can start harvesting and juicing it. A 15-inch diameter tray should give you about 6 shots. Some trays are sectioned into 6, which makes it super easy to measure your shots.

Now you are ready to start juicing your wheatgrass. 1 shot should be plenty, but you can consume as much as you want. Make sure that you take your shot of wheatgrass on an empty stomach for optimal effectiveness.

Chapter 7: In a Nutshell

1. Get a blood test to make sure you are not lacking any nutrients that could be contributing to your anxiety. These blood tests would consist of B1, B6, B12, zinc, iron, ferritin, and vitamin D. Other vitamins that are important for brain health are magnesium and omega 3 fatty acids.

2. Sugar is a drug in disguise. Binging on sugar can cause racing thoughts, lack of focus, loss of memory, brain fog, and poor digestion, all of which can make your bossy brain bossier.

3. The keto diet is known for its weight loss abilities, but its effect on brain health is commonly overlooked. Incorporating a low carb diet like the keto diet can improve brain function, reduce inflammation, improve digestion, and increase oxygen to the brain.

4. Inflammation interferes with the neural pathways. This interference blocks healthy nerve activity and the happy chemicals from reaching the brain's receptors.

5. Heavy metals such as mercury, aluminum, and lead can make its way into the human body. These can all affect the nervous system, so it would be best to incorporate a heavy metal detox every so often. You can detox through chelating with cilantro or chlorella, or by consuming wheatgrass.

Chapter 8: The Happy Chemicals

The four main chemicals that contribute to positive emotions are serotonin, dopamine, endorphins, and oxytocin. Serotonin contributes to wellbeing, happiness, and mood stabilization. Dopamine contributes to wellbeing, pleasure, and satisfaction, in addition to playing a motivational role in the brain's reward system. Endorphins are considered a natural pain reliever and they actually have a very similar structure to morphine. This is because it activates opiate receptors in the brain that help alleviate discomfort. Endorphins also contribute to a sense of wellbeing, euphoria, and relaxation. Oxytocin, also known as the cuddle hormone, plays a role in love, social bonding, and trust.

An interesting thing to note is that 90% of serotonin and 50% of dopamine is not made in the brain, it's actually made in the intestinal lining. Out of all the communication between the brain and gut, only 10% is information flowing from the brain to the gut, while 90% is flowing from the gut to the brain. Isn't that fascinating? That means the gut dominates this relationship, and that's why it's sometimes referred to as the second brain.

The intestines are lined with enteroendocrine cells which are capable of releasing 20 different types of hormones into the bloodstream when called upon. The intestines produce a healthy amount of serotonin and dopamine when good bacteria line the intestines. Most of serotonin is stored in the gut, while the majority of dopamine is stored in the brain. An unhealthy gut interferes with the production and distribution of these happy chemicals. For example, antibiotics are great at killing bad bacteria, but they take down the good bacteria with them. This leaves the body vulnerable to microbial imbalances. If the good bacteria are killed off from the intestinal lining, then the body can't properly produce enough serotonin and dopamine. Being that the majority of these happy chemicals are produced in the intestines, it's no wonder why someone can have impairments in mood and anxiety as a result of a digestive imbalance.

Now let's explore how we can ensure that our body is harmoniously abundant in these happy chemicals.

Serotonin so Sweet – Keeps Me Awake, and Helps Me Sleep

Serotonin is responsible for many different functions in the human body, from emotional well-being to motor skills. An imbalance or lack of serotonin can wreak havoc throughout the body and may even have a connection to neurological disorders, such as epilepsy, Parkinson's, MS, ALS, ADHD, autism, and most notably, anxiety and depression.

Unfortunately, there are no specific blood tests to determine serotonin levels stored in the body. The current test available only measures the amount of serotonin in the blood, which doesn't do much good. So, let's take a look at what causes a serotonin deficiency, the symptoms, and how we can boost the levels in our body.

Causes of a Serotonin Deficiency:

1. **Digestive issues** can affect serotonin production being that 90% is produced in the gut.

2. **Fluctuating hormones** caused by hormone replacement therapy, PMS, pregnancy, and old age can interfere with serotonin production, release, and distribution.

3. **Lack of sunlight** - Sunlight triggers the release of serotonin throughout the day, which helps boost our mood while keeping us calm and focused. Serotonin also triggers the release of melatonin at night, which helps us sleep. A lack of sunlight would interfere with this process, resulting in a lack of serotonin.

4. **A poor diet** can contribute to inflammation and digestive issues which can interfere with the production and distribution of serotonin. Someone who eats a lot of processed foods and sugars are at most risk. Bad bacteria feeds on sugar, which creates an abundance of them in the gut. This leaves the good bacteria vulnerable for takeover. Inflammation causes blockages by interfering with the pathways that serotonin uses to get to the brain. Incorporating anti-inflammatory foods can help reverse the damage caused by inflammation. These foods would consist of fatty fish containing omega 3's, dark leafy greens, ginger, turmeric, nuts, and seeds. Poultry, such as turkey, contains a chemical called tryptophan, which can help boost serotonin.

5. **Chronic stress and anxiety** shut off serotonin and dopamine production so that the body can maintain stress hormones to keep you prepared for "flight or fight." The body doesn't want to keep you calm and happy if there is an imminent threat. It wants to keep you alert and ready.

6. **Illicit drugs and some medications** could drain your serotonin levels by continuously overusing them. Our body stores serotonin, so these reserves would have to be replenished in order to maintain a healthy supply.

Serotonin Deficiency Symptoms:

1. **Anxiety** can contribute to low serotonin, while low serotonin can contribute to anxiety. Either way, the relationship is usually

125

codependent, meaning that it's a vicious cycle between low serotonin and bouts of anxiety, because they both fuel each other. Specific anxiety disorders known to be connected to low serotonin include OCD, PTSD, panic disorder, and social anxiety.

2. **Depression** can also get stuck in a perpetual codependent relationship with serotonin, because low levels could lead to anxiety, as well as more depression.

3. **Fatigue** can be a symptom of low serotonin, but it can also cause insomnia which can contribute to more fatigue. This can be extremely frustrating to someone who feels tired all day but can't sleep at night. The reason for this is that serotonin is responsible for both wakefulness and sleep. Serotonin helps you stay alert and focused throughout the day, but also helps produce the melatonin that helps you sleep. Therefore, a lack of serotonin can make you feel tired during the day but won't be able to trigger enough melatonin at night to help you sleep.

4. **Getting lost in nighttime anxiety**. Have you ever found that your anxiety or negative thinking is heightened during the night? The amygdala, which is responsible for the "flight or fight" response, is highly active during REM sleep. This makes us vulnerable to anxiety in the middle of the night. Serotonin stimulates the release of melatonin, which helps promote sleep. Someone with anxiety most likely has low serotonin levels that drop even lower throughout the night. This could be the reason for elevated anxiety and excessive worry that occurs in the middle of the night. I can't tell you how many times I've woken up in the middle of night panicking, researching symptoms, and believing the worst-case scenario, only to wake up in the morning with a fraction of that anxiety. Try to remember this next time you get lost in nighttime anxiety.

5. **Loss of motivation or interest** in activities you previously enjoyed.

6. **Memory loss or learning issues** can be a result of the lack of focus that comes along with a serotonin deficiency. Studies are finding a correlation between low serotonin and Alzheimer's, dementia, and other neurodegenerative disorders. Increasing serotonin levels could potentially help alleviate symptoms, as well as the progression of some of these diseases.

7. **Chronic pain** can indicate low serotonin due to the effect it has on pain perception and muscle control. For this reason, those who suffer from fibromyalgia or migraines could benefit from increasing their serotonin levels.

8. **Constipation or IBS** indicates abnormal gut function, which could be a result of a lack of intestinal contractions and mucus secretions related to a lack of serotonin.

9. **Overeating or lack of appetite** are messages sent from the gut to the brain, which are both associated with abnormal gut function. Serotonin receptors in the intestines are responsible for sending information to the brain regarding satisfaction and fullness. A lack of serotonin production can cause mixed communications to the brain resulting in food cravings, especially for carbohydrates and sugars. This disconnect can also contribute to a lack of appetite that could possibly result in eating disorders, such as anorexia or bulimia.

How to Boost Serotonin

1. **Nutrition** - Substitute sugars and processed foods for anti-inflammatory foods, such as salmon, leafy greens, nuts and seeds.

2. **Exercise** increases tryptophan in the brain, which is an amino acid responsible for serotonin production. Shoot for aerobic exercises that get your heart rate up.

3. **Positive Mood** - Try to stay positive, laugh, watch comedies, and try to avoid anything negative, such as the news or dark shows and movies.

4. **Bright light** - Sunlight notifies your body that it's daytime. This triggers the production of serotonin to improve energy and focus.

5. **Probiotics** can help increase tryptophan, which is a chemical that's converted to serotonin in the brain. They also help improve the digestive tract, which is where 90% of serotonin is produced and stored.

6. **Yoga, meditation, massage and relaxation music** helps reduce the stress hormones in your body, while increasing serotonin and dopamine production.

7. **Supplements such as 5HTP, tryptophan, or combining magnesium and vitamin B6**. Magnesium helps regulate serotonin, while B6 helps the body utilize it. Make sure that 5HTP doesn't conflict with any medications you may be taking. *Do not take 5HTP if you are currently taking any medication for depression or anxiety. Too much serotonin can cause serotonin syndrome, which can be very dangerous. 5HTP also reduces the amount of dopamine in your body, so you may want to consider increasing your dopamine levels with l-tyrosine while on 5HTP. I do not recommend taking 5HTP on a regular basis. It should only be used as needed. If you find that your anxiety is worsening with 5HTP, then you may have too much serotonin in your body.

Dopamine Junkie

Dopamine is a neurotransmitter in the brain that sends messages to nerve cells. It plays an important role in the brain's reward system, which gives you the motivation to seek pleasure. It's also associated with mood, learning, memory, motor control, and more. 50% of dopamine is produced in the brain, while the other 50% is produced in the gut.

Dopamine is responsible for both emotional and physical well-being. For this reason, there's an extensive list of symptoms associated with a dopamine deficiency. Balanced dopamine levels are vital for mood, sleep, memory, learning, concentration, and motor control. It's also responsible for the pleasure and anticipation of receiving rewards, which can contribute to both positive and negative behavior. However, dopamine is released at a more moderate rate when associated with positive behavior, while negative behavior usually triggers too much release all at once. Low dopamine levels have also been associated with many mental disorders, such as anxiety, depression, Parkinson's, addictions, schizophrenia, and psychosis.

There is testing available that could determine a dopamine imbalance, however the results are unreliable and are not commonly offered. You may be better off examining whether you have a history of addiction, poor diet, obesity, impaired mood, and digestive issues. Any of these issues can indicate a dopamine deficiency.

Causes of a Dopamine Deficiency

1. **Drug and alcohol abuse** interfere with the amount of dopamine needed for the brain to function properly. Drugs and alcohol trigger an excessive release of dopamine, which is why you get that high feeling. Once your brain stops releasing dopamine, you start to crash. Continuous use of drugs and alcohol depletes dopamine reserves, which makes it harder to achieve the positive effects of this happy chemical. Dopamine receptors also begin to shut down, making it harder for your brain to absorb dopamine.

2. **Obesity and overeating** can be just as damaging as drugs and alcohol when it comes to dopamine levels. Every time you eat, your body releases dopamine, which is constantly depleting your reserves. The brain's reward system also begins to associate overeating as a reward, which makes the person want to eat more to keep achieving this satisfaction. In addition to depleted reserves, the receptors also become damaged. This could be due to the brain trying to overcompensate for a continuous overflow of dopamine, resulting in overworked receptors.

3. **Diets high in sugar and saturated fat** continuously trigger excessive amounts of dopamine, thereby producing the desire to consume more and more. However, the more you eat, the more you release dopamine, which is exhausting your reserves and receptors. This eventually depletes your reserves and makes your receptors lazy or inactive. Being that dopamine is connected to your brain's reward system, you don't want to trick your brain into thinking that eating sugars and saturated fats are a reward.

4. **Diets low in protein** can lead to a lack of l-tyrosine, which is an amino acid essential to building dopamine.

5. **Poor diet** resulting in a lack of B vitamins, zinc, iron, copper, and magnesium. You should focus on increasing these nutrients because they are known to help boost dopamine levels.

6. **Digestive Issues** can lead to a deficiency because 50% of dopamine is produced in the gut. If your digestive system is not functioning properly, then you may not be producing enough dopamine, or the neural pathways to the brain may be blocked as a result of inflammation.

7. **Chronic Stress** leads to a consistent overflow of stress hormones, while suppressing calming hormones like serotonin and dopamine.

Dopamine Deficiency Symptoms

- Depression
- Bad memory, especially short-term memory, such as forgetting the first part of your sentence
- Body tremors, such as shaking hands
- Difficulty eating or swallowing due to a lack of contractions in the esophagus
- Muscle spasms, muscle stiffness, cramps, and tremors
- Constipation
- Loss of balance when standing or walking

- Uncontrollable eye movements
- Difficulty sleeping
- Gastroesophageal reflux disease or GERD
- Frequent pneumonia occurrences
- Difficulty speaking, articulating words, or speaking slower than usual
- Hallucinations, delusions, or a lack of awareness
- Anxiousness
- Low energy and fatigue
- An inability to focus
- Mood swings, lack of motivation, hopelessness, sadness, and low self esteem

How to Boost Dopamine

1. **Nutrition** - Try to limit sugars and saturated fats as much as possible. You can start by limiting your consumption of processed food and sugar. At the same time, you should increase your intake of vegetables, healthy grains, legumes, nuts, seeds, and unprocessed meats, such as chicken and fish. The goal here is to increase B vitamins, copper, iron, zinc, and magnesium in your body. These vitamins and minerals help facilitate the production of dopamine, and a lack of them can contribute to a deficiency.

2. **Tyrosine** converts to dopamine in the body, and you can find this important amino acid in beef, pork, salmon, chicken, tofu, and beans.

3. **Probiotics** are a great way to improve digestion which can ensure that you produce enough dopamine. They can also reduce inflammation, ensuring that your neural pathways are not blocked.

4. **Exercise** increases new brain cells, prevents neurodegenerative disease, and stimulates the production of the happy chemicals.

5. **Sleep** is extremely important because it allows your body to detox, heal, and regenerate itself. This keeps the neural pathways to the brain functioning properly. Dopamine needs these pathways to be clear in order to make its way to the brain.

6. **Yoga, meditation, massage, and listening to music** can help you relax and destress. Stress inhibits dopamine production, so it's important to reduce your stress levels as much as possible.

7. **Setting achievable goals** will boost dopamine, while keeping you motivated to succeed. This can be as simple as making a list of things you need to do for the week. You'll find satisfaction in marking them off as you complete them.

8. **Supplements such as L-tyrosine** can be taken to increase dopamine levels, which is a natural amino acid found in protein rich foods. L-tyrosine should be taken in the morning and on an empty stomach for optimal effectiveness. *L-tyrosine should not be taken long term and should only be taken as needed. Make sure that l-tyrosine will not interfere with any medications that you may be taking. Those who are pregnant or who have an overactive thyroid or graves' disease should avoid L-tyrosine.

OCD and Dopamine Imbalance

My brother suffers from OCD which is what got me thinking about the possible connection between OCD and a dopamine imbalance. OCD is characterized by irrational intrusive thoughts or obsessions, which usually lead to compulsive behaviors. There is fear and anxiety associated with these repetitive thoughts, while acting out the compulsions helps provide relief.

Dopamine is closely related to the pleasure and reward portion of the brain. It is also responsible for creating the anticipation and motivation to seek these rewards, with the expectation of feeling pleasure once they are received. This reward system is important for us to be driven individuals with a motivation to succeed in everyday life. Dopamine, when in balance, is a great contributor to overall well-being.

However, this reward system can get out of control when there is a dopamine imbalance mixed with someone who is susceptible to addictive behaviors, such as someone with OCD. The person with OCD experiences obsessive thoughts, which creates the anticipation of avoiding these thoughts through acting out certain behaviors known as compulsions. The problem is that they continue to experience more obsessive thoughts because their anticipation wasn't followed up with an actual award, or it was short lived. Therefore, the cycle of expectation and the letdown continues, which keeps the person with OCD repeating these compulsive behaviors in anticipation of a reward that's never achieved. This expectation triggers the continuous release of dopamine, which can cause high levels of dopamine in the brain. This continuous release can deplete the reserves and exhaust the overstimulated dopamine receptors. Therefore, someone who suffers from extreme OCD can end up with low levels of dopamine reserves and overstimulated receptors. This puts them at risk of becoming susceptible to drug, alcohol, sugar or any other addictions in search of more rewards.

My brother's OCD tends to flare up during stressful times or when his substance abuse gets out of control. Being that he's suffered from OCD for most of his life, he's always been more susceptible to addictions. He's been substance free for years now and has yet to experience a major OCD episode. However, there were times in the past when his addictions would get out of control, and so would his OCD, keeping him in a perpetual cycle.

Overcoming Addiction and Rebalancing Dopamine

When someone suffers from long term addictions, they experience a dopamine imbalance in the brain. This results in a lack of motivation and makes it harder to feel pleasure in normal day new experiences. This is especially true for those who are overcoming and abstaining from their addictions. It's in this time that healing needs to occur. Luckily, dopamine levels can be restored, and receptors can heal themselves, but it's important to remain abstinent in order for recovery to occur. What needs to happen during this time is the brain needs to rewire itself, so it stops associating addictions with pleasure. In other words, the person will need to rewire their brain to stop releasing dopamine when they think of their addiction. It can take time for this to occur, so patience is vital when overcoming addictions. According to the "Recovery Research Institute" it can take 14 months for dopamine rebalancing to occur, given the person is abstinent during this time.

It's the same idea for those suffering from OCD. They must abstain from their compulsions for a significant amount of time in order to weaken the obsession. This retrains the brain to stop associating compulsions with a reward, so the brain will stop releasing dopamine when thinking about or acting out compulsions.

During abstinence, it's important to try to increase dopamine levels in healthier ways which we've gone over earlier. Some of these consist of nutrition, especially increasing l-tyrosine consumption, exercise, sleep, relaxation, and finding more positive things that bring you pleasure, such as immersing yourself in nature. Another thing to consider is going on a purpose driven journey. Living out your purpose is an excellent way to beat addictions because purpose gives your life meaning. Purpose can activate the brain's pleasure reward system in a positive way, and it won't come with a hangover the next day. We'll explore purpose more in the "Live Your Life on Purpose" chapter of this book.

Dopamine Detox

Dopamine fasting or a dopamine diet can be done to rebalance the brains motivation-reward system. The fast involves abstaining from all activities that involve pleasure, including food, alcohol, sex, masturbation, social media, video games, TV, and talking. The fast can be done for one day on a monthly basis. The only thing you should allow yourself to do is drink water, be in nature, do some light exercise, meditate, and write in a journal.

Both positive and negative behaviors release dopamine. The difference is that positive behaviors release less and at a more moderate rate than negative behaviors do. Negative behaviors provide a dopamine rush all at once. All humans have a natural dopamine addiction, and this is why we're suckers for instant gratification. We're dopamine fiends that just want more and more. But it is possible to tame our dopamine addiction, so we experience more pleasure doing the healthier things in life. This can be done through dopamine fasting.

The point is to cut out all over stimulating activities so that your brain stops excessively pumping out dopamine, especially with negative behaviors. We can choose what our brain connects with pleasure by first eliminating all pleasure inducing behaviors, and then reintroducing the healthy ones back first. You can slowly bring back negative behaviors, but only if the positive ones take up the majority of your time. The dopamine rush resulting from negative behaviors makes us lazy and less motivated to participate in more positive behaviors. For example, a slice of pizza pumps out way more dopamine than a salad, so your brain automatically wants the pizza every time. But when you eliminate pizza from your diet, your brain will start to associate healthy meals like a salad with pleasure again.

The point is that you want to bore yourself enough to give yourself a chance to reset your pleasure-reward system. This allows you to associate pleasure with the healthier things in life, rather than the unhealthy things. For example, if you're trying to eliminate sugar from your diet, then a dopamine fast will give you a better chance at achieving this. Have you ever gone hungry long enough to the point that you were starving and willing to eat just about anything? Even plain rice sounds delicious when you're starving. This is all connected to the dopamine's pleasure-reward system in the brain. You want to starve yourself of pleasure, so your brain stops taking advantage of the healthier things in life. Your brain will have a new appreciation for positive behaviors as long as you don't overwhelm it with the negative ones. *Remember, negative behaviors make your brain lazy.

Endorphins - Natures Opioid

Endorphins are a natural source of pain and stress relief. They work by binding to opioid receptors in the brain, which blocks the perception of pain. Endorphins produce the same effect that morphine and codeine do, by alleviating pain and creating a euphoric feeling. Isn't that wild? Think runners high. It's a real thing!

Endorphins in the brain can be measured through positron emission tomography (PET) scans done before and after exercise. The number of endorphins present after an intense workout can be an indication of whether there's a deficiency or not.

Causes of Endorphin Deficiency:

- Lack of exercise
- Obesity
- Substance abuse and addiction
- Endorphin Deficiency Symptoms
- Anxiety
- Depression
- Fibromyalgia or migraines
- Moodiness and emotionally unstable
- Extreme Pain sensitivity
- Addiction for alcohol, drugs, and sugar
- Impulsive behavior
- Insomnia

How to Boost Endorphins:

- Exercise
- Acupuncture
- Yoga, meditation, and massage
- Creativity, such as making music or art
- Eating foods rich in protein, vitamin C and omega 3 fatty acids
- Having Sex
- Eating dark chocolate

- Eating spicy foods
- Laughing
- Supplements, such as DL-Phenylalanine (DLPA), which is a natural amino acid found in protein rich foods, can produce the same effect that endorphins can. Check to make sure this supplement doesn't interfere with any medications you may be taking.

Oxytocin AKA the Love Drug

Oxytocin is known as the "cuddle hormone" or "love drug" and is produced by the hypothalamus and secreted by the pituitary glands. This hormone is released when people snuggle or during social bonding, especially with those in your inner circle or in romantic relationships. Oxytocin also plays a big role in giving birth and nursing, by stimulating contractions and releasing breast milk.

Oxytocin can affect individuals differently when it comes to social bonding and relationships, based on their childhood experiences with their family. Someone who was nurtured as a child will most likely experience positive emotional connections when the hormone is triggered. Someone who wasn't nurtured as a child might exhibit disconnectedness or negative reactions when triggered. For example, someone who was neglected as a child might be uncomfortable with affection or physical touch, resulting in negative feelings associated with affection. Someone who was shown a lot of love as a child would respond to affection more positively as an adult.

Oxytocin deficiencies are associated with many different mental health disorders, such as anxiety, depression, autism, schizophrenia, and other mood disorders. These disorders all have a societal disconnect in common.

Oxytocin levels can be checked through blood tests although it's not that common. You can determine whether you may have a deficiency based on the symptoms below. There are also ways to boost oxytocin, which can be done whether you are deficient or not.

Causes of Oxytocin Deficiency:

- Chronic stress
- Lack of social bonding with family or friends, loneliness
- Anger and fear
- Detachment from relationships
- Drug abuse

Oxytocin Deficiency Symptoms:

- Walking away from relationships easily
- Detachment from others
- Displaying a lack of compassion
- Inability to feel affectionate
- Fearful or anxious
- Having sex to fulfill a basic need rather than an emotional connection
- Unhappiness in life
- Insomnia
- Muscle aches
- Excessive sugar cravings
- Low libido

How to Boost Oxytocin:

- Increase social bonding
- Being in a relationship
- Cuddling, snuggling, being intimate, hugging
- Laughing, socializing, playing, giving
- Massage, music, singing
- Exercise
- Visiting family
- Human interaction, trust, and intimacy

Birth Control

You may not realize that your birth control could be feeding your bossy brain, especially if you are predisposed to mood disorders. I mean how can it not, right? It's a hormone disruptor that mimics progesterone and estrogen, which interferes with the body's natural hormone production. Normally, these hormones rise and fall throughout the month. However, birth control keeps estrogen levels artificially high throughout the month to trick your body into thinking it's pregnant. These artificially high levels of estrogen significantly increase serotonin levels, which is why some women may experience less anxiety with birth control. However, too much serotonin can lead to overactive nerve cells, which would result in a bossier brain.

It's known that birth control can cause mood swings, but there's very little research on how birth control can actually affect the mind. I know from personal experience that birth control can definitely contribute to anxiety. The first time I had one of the worst panic attacks of my life was when I started taking birth control. I was experiencing mood swings, depression, and major brain fog. I kept fighting with my boyfriend at the time and found myself hysterically crying over the most tedious things. I couldn't control my emotions. The constant brain fog made me literally feel like I was losing my mind. Eventually, all these emotions exploded into that massive panic attack that I had at 27 years old. I couldn't breathe, I thought I was going crazy, my heart was racing, all while I was going through an emotional roller coaster. I wanted to crawl out of my skin. I knew it was a result of birth control because I had never experienced anything like it, and I had just started taking the pills 3 weeks prior. Some women might say that birth control reduced their anxiety, but this was not the case for me. I believe it all comes down to the individual, so if you feel like birth control may be feeding your bossy brain, then it probably is. I would suggest finding a non-hormonal birth control as soon as possible.

Most people know that antibiotics are terrible for your digestive system. But did you know that birth control can be just as bad? Birth control wipes out the good guys in your gut, similar to antibiotics. Birth control can contribute to leaky gut, IBS, candida overgrowth, and Crohn's disease, all of which are related to the gut. Our intestines are lined with hormone receptors and adding hormones to your body at elevated levels can cause all kinds of digestive issues. This leaves our gut susceptible to bacteria and yeast overgrowth. As we've already learned, there's a close connection between brain and gut health. The bottom line is that we need our digestive system to be in optimal health in order to keep our bossy brain in check.

The Woman's Cycle - PMS

Women's hormones fluctuate throughout the month in order to facilitate pregnancy. Unfortunately, mood and anxiety levels tend to mimic the rise and fall of these hormones. Let's take a look at what goes on during a woman's 28-day cycle, starting with the first day of her period.

Week 1

By day 1, estrogen is at its lowest. During these 7 days, estrogen levels will increase thereby boosting serotonin, providing enhanced mood, as well as physical and mental energy.

Week 2

Day 8 through ovulation. Estrogen continues to rise until ovulation occurs. This increase in estrogen keeps the mind sharp and clear.

Week 3

Occurs the day after ovulation begins. At this point, progesterone rises, while estrogen falls. Serotonin levels fall with the decrease in estrogen; however, this can be offset by the rise in progesterone. Progesterone has a sedating effect that can assist with relaxation. As a result, some may experience anxiety and fluctuations in mood during ovulation. Within a few days of ovulation, estrogen will begin to rise again. Therefore, if the drop in estrogen did increase your anxiety during ovulation, it should subside within a few days as it begins to increase again. *One more thing to note is that progesterone makes you more sensitive to drops in blood sugar. If you feel anxious during this time of your menstruation cycle, make sure to keep your blood sugar up. You can do this by eating a piece of fruit.

Week 4

During the 7 days prior to menstruation, estrogen and progesterone plummet which can contribute to PMS. Estrogen facilitates serotonin, while progesterone produces a sedative effect. As a result of this drop, you may experience PMS symptoms, such as anxiety, light depression, mood swings, insomnia, sleep disruptions, fatigue, overeating, and hot flashes.

The good news is that PMS can be managed through diet and supplementation. As we learned earlier, a healthy gut can keep the bossy brain in check. There are so many good reasons why we should focus on improving our diet.

Here are some things to consider in order to get your PMS in control:

1. **Iron** – Make sure you're not iron deficient by checking your iron and ferritin levels. Make sure your doctor checks you for both iron and ferritin. Ferritin stores iron in your body and releases it as necessary. Low reserves can cause all kinds of issues. Also, consider getting a ferritin test while you're on your period, because this is when your levels will be at the lowest. This will be a clear indication of whether you really have a deficiency or not. Symptoms associated with low iron levels can consist of anxiety, PMS, poor circulation, heart palpitations, shortness of breath, sleep deprivation, and fatigue. Women are at most risk of an iron deficiency as a result of blood loss through menstruation, especially those with heavy periods and endometriosis.

2. **Eliminate triggers** – Cut down or eliminate caffeine, alcohol, nicotine, and sugar. If you find it hard to cut down or eliminate these stimulants, then try your best to at least avoid them starting 7 days before your period. This will help keep your mental health in check while your hormones are all out of whack.

3. **Eat clean and healthy food** – Increase consumption of fruits, vegetables, nuts, legumes, eggs, chicken, and fish.

4. **Exercise** can boost serotonin and endorphins. Serotonin can help improve your mood, as well as sleep. Endorphins are a natural source of pain and stress relief. It works by binding to opioid receptors in the brain which blocks the perception of pain. Endorphins produce the same effect that morphine and codeine do, by alleviating pain and creating a euphoric feeling. Lower levels of endorphins could be associated with impaired mood, depression, anxiety, migraines and painful periods. Exercise can also help alleviate bloating and increase oxygen within the body. Low blood oxygen levels can contribute to mental health issues and cognitive impairment. Lack of oxygen to the pelvic area is what contributes to period cramps, so exercise and eliminating smoking or anything else that restricts oxygen can really help.

5. **Sunlight** can boost vitamin D and serotonin levels, helping with mood and sleep cycles.

6. **PMS vitamins** – These vitamins can help alleviate symptoms associated with PMS and can be purchased online.

7. **Supplements that help with PMS** – Consider taking a supplement that has calcium, vitamin D, magnesium and B6. Vitamin D helps regulate mood swings, bloating, and fatigue, in addition to promoting calcium absorption. Magnesium helps regulate serotonin, while vitamin B6 helps the body utilize it.

Understanding how hormones affect your body is key to balancing out your bossy brain. Women who experience PMS should keep an eye on their mental status throughout their cycle to determine whether low progesterone and serotonin could be the culprit. There are plenty of period tracker apps that can help you track where you are in your monthly cycle. Suffering from fluctuating hormones doesn't need to be inevitable, and can be managed through diet, supplementing, and exercise.

Chapter 8: In a Nutshell

1. A good balance of happy chemicals is necessary in order to have a healthy functioning brain. These chemicals consist of serotonin, dopamine, endorphins, and oxytocin. Make sure to keep your digestive tract healthy, avoid drugs, and exercise plenty in order to ensure that these chemicals thrive in your body. If you feel like you may be deficient, you can use supplements to help increase your levels.

2. Birth control has a negative effect on the digestive tract and pumps artificial hormones in the body. These hormones consist of estrogen and progesterone, which boost serotonin levels and have a mood boosting relaxation effect. However, too much serotonin can lead to serotonin syndrome, leaving you with overexcited nerve cells, which can worsen anxiety. Therefore, birth control can either worsen anxiety symptoms or make them better. It all depends on the person. If you think that it might be making your anxiety worse, then it probably is.

3. Women's hormones fluctuate throughout her cycle. Unfortunately, mood and anxiety tend to mimic the rise and fall of these hormones. If you find that you may be experiencing anxiety as a result of these fluctuations, then you can use supplements, such as 5HTP to help relieve these symptoms.

Chapter 9: Spirituality - Faith Over Fear

"Release all negativity and adopt a mindset of love and peace. In the end, this is all that exists in the afterlife" - Bob Marley

I was taught to believe in God at a very young age. My family belonged to a Christian Greek Orthodox church, which we would attend every so often. Our priest would speak in an Armenian dialect that made it hard to interpret, which left me uninterested. I never actually read the Bible, other than biblical stories in a children's book that my dad got me when I was younger. I was taught that God watches over us, asks us not to sin, and answers our prayers. So, I would pray. "God, are you listening? Please take these terrible diseases away from me. I promise I will never be bad again!" I would then go to bed, wake up the next morning, and run straight to the bathroom to see if God answered my prayers. Hmm … yeah, the "symptoms" were still there. "God, you failed me!" I didn't understand how to truly connect and communicate with the other side. The fact that God wasn't talking to me or immediately answering my prayers, made me lose faith. I would remember going to bed every night wondering what death was like. I imagined it as darkness and nothingness. Dirt in the ground. The thought of nothingness after death terrified me, which spiraled into more fear. This fear fueled my anxiety for almost 18 years.

In my mid-20's I finally started opening up to my friends about my hypochondria. They had already known about my panic attacks, but not that I was terrified that I was dying of numerous diseases. One of my friends was shocked at what I was telling her. She told me that if I kept worrying about diseases, then I might actually get one. She explained how we manifest what we think about. I then did some research on the concept and was astonished at what I was finding. I started to read book after book regarding the law of attraction, to permanently engrain this concept in my brain. By being mindful of my thoughts, I was able to establish a new positive way of thinking. I noticed good things started to happen, and I was attracting everything I was thinking about. There were signs everywhere that the universe was really working with me. This allowed me to get more control when it came to my hypochondria. At the time, I didn't really understand the metaphysics behind the law of attraction. I just knew that your thoughts become your reality.

Spiritual Awakening

I experienced an emotionally tough time a few years back, when my ex and I broke up. We had been together for 5 years, and knew each other for 15, so yeah … it was a pretty tough breakup. We both wanted different things, and neither of us were willing to compromise, so we had to come to terms with the fact that the relationship wasn't going to work. The toughest part was that I was breaking up with someone that I was still in love with, but I knew there was no other choice. It was a pretty tough time in my life, and I was having a hard time handling my emotions.

About 6 months later I was talking to a friend of mine living in New York. He told me that he had been traveling the world, learning about spirituality and metaphysics. Something clicked in me that day. I've believed in universal energy for many years now, so why was it that I was focusing on what I don't want, rather than what I do want? So, I dusted off my old books and found "Manifest Your Destiny" by Wayne Dyer. I hadn't read the book yet, so I was excited to dive right in. I loved the book so much that I read it twice. Wayne teaches you how to get in tune with the universal energy in order to attract what you want. He emphasizes the connection between manifestation and the spiritual world, while teaching you how to embody energetically, whatever it is you desire.

Although I loved Wayne's work, I really wanted to connect with a younger author that teaches similar philosophies with a modern twist. I knew exactly what type of book I was looking for, but I didn't know how I was going to find it. So, I set my intention and started searching for a new book to help guide me on my universal journey. I suddenly came across "Super Attracter" written by Gabrielle Bernstein. I remembered Gabrielle from her book I purchased around 10 years ago, called "Add More Ing to Your Life." I thought to myself, "Wow, she's still around and she's made so many books since then." How interesting that I stumbled upon this book on metaphysics that she just recently published. So, I gave it a go! I was loving the book and couldn't believe I found the exact type of book and author that I was searching for. About halfway through the book, she started talking about spirit guides, and how we all have them. She mentions how she had a close friendship with Wayne Dyer before he passed away. She also mentions that she believes that he is one of her spirit guides, and that Wayne loves to offer guidance from beyond to anyone who seeks it. I thought to myself, "Whoa ... wait a second ... could it be that Wayne guided me to Gabby's book?" I knew there was going to be a major significance in this book that I really needed to pay attention to.

So, I read the book a few times, and decided it was time to learn more about spirit guides. I told my friend from NY that I just learned about spirit guides, and that I was searching for the perfect book to help me channel them. He said he had never heard about spirit guides, but that he does support my journey. A few days later, he sent me an image of a book called "Open to Channel: How to Connect with Your Guide" by Sanaya Roman and Duane Packer. He noticed the book while he was sitting in the sauna at his gym that day. There was no one in the sauna with him, just the book. Someone must have left it behind. The message was loud and clear, and it was meant to be delivered to me. When he told me about the book, I busted out with excitement knowing the book was sent to me by my guides. The book teaches you details on how to channel, what you can ask, what you can expect, and how the guides communicate with you.

Once I was done reading the book, I knew it was time to start channeling. I laid in my bed, closed my eyes, and put my eye mask on. I started with deep slow breaths to get into a state of relaxation. Gabby says to channel spirit guides by saying the following, "Spirit guides of the highest truth and compassion ..." So that's exactly what I did. I continued to repeat it for another few minutes, when I suddenly felt a rush of goosebumps throughout my body. The contractions were so intense and uncontrollable, I had never felt anything like it. Once the goosebumps lightened up, I noticed a feeling of transition to what felt like another realm. It felt as if I entered outer space, and the concept of time had stopped. Let me tell you, it freaked me the hell out! I ripped off my eye mask and jumped out of bed. I couldn't believe what I had just experienced. It was as if I had awoken to a whole new world. I was scared of what I had just experienced but intrigued at the same time. I knew I had to try it again.

So, here I was excited to channel my guides again. I had the same experience as the day before, but this time, I was able to follow through. I used some of the time to show gratitude to my guides by thanking them for their support and guidance. I then asked my guides to show me a sign if I made a mistake breaking up with my ex-boyfriend. I asked them to show me a butterfly if it was a mistake and a deer if it was not. I had received a phone call from my friend while I was in my meditation, so I decided to give her a call back once I was done. She asked me what I was doing, and I told her that I just got out of my meditation. She cracked a joke at me and said, "Oh, so what? Did a deer pop its head through your window?" I was in shock! I couldn't believe what she had just said. "What did you say?" I asked her. So, she said it again, "Did a deer pop its head through your window?" Wow, my guides were telling me loud and clear that I had made the right decision leaving my ex-boyfriend. And that's all it took. I was a believer, and I knew my life would never be the same.

Communicating with Your Spirit Guides

Guidance can come from within you or external factors, and they usually appear synchronistically. The guidance that comes from within is that feeling you get in your gut, also known as your intuition. Sometimes we ask questions in hopes of seeking the answers we want to hear, but deep down, we already know the answer. That sense of "inner knowing" is guidance from your guides. Guides don't need to use words, they communicate subliminally, which are translated into our thoughts. Think about your relationship with your dog. Dogs don't need to use words to communicate with us. We have such a close bond with them that there is an unspoken understanding between us. The connection is based on intuition, energy, senses, emotions, and feelings. Animals are more sensitive to the spiritual world, because they must rely on their intuition to survive. They don't doubt their intuition like we do. The fact that they have to use their senses to communicate makes them hypersensitive to energetic fields.

Signs from within can also reveal themselves through emotions that feel out of place. For example, if while driving, you suddenly get this feeling or an inclination to slow down, pull over, or take an alternative route, then it's time to pay attention to what your gut might be telling you. Another example is being in a perfectly safe place, such as a grocery store, yet you have this slight uneasy feeling in the pit of your stomach, or you have an inclination to leave the store. Your gut might be telling you that your presence is needed or would benefit from being somewhere else at that very moment. Pay attention to what your gut might be telling you, especially if the emotions you are experiencing are not conducive to the environment you're currently in.

Note that It's important to make sure the emotions are coming from intuition, rather than anxiety. You can differentiate intuition from anxiety by determining whether the emotion is based on the present moment or sometime in the future. Remember that intuition lives in the present, while anxiety lives in the future. Also, intuition comes from a clear, calm, relaxed and gentle place. Anxiety involves fear, panic, worry, and confusion. So, let's look back at the driving scenario. If while driving, your heart rate suddenly increases, and you get this feeling that you are going to get in an accident if you don't slow down, then this is coming from a place of anxiety, rather than intuition. Intuition will feel like a gentle nudge of "inner knowing", whether you're headed in either the right direction or not.

Signs from Your Guides

1. **People** such as friends, family, co-workers, acquaintances, or even strangers can be your messenger from your guide. Think back to my friend who mentioned the deer or my other friend who randomly came across the spirit guide book that I was meant to read. This is especially true if the person is operating at a similar vibration as you are.

2. **Recurring events** - Think about a question you may have asked your guides. They could be answering you through an animal's symbolic meaning. For example, hummingbirds can symbolize a change that needs to occur in your life. Last year I found myself really unhappy in my corporate job. It felt like I was spending all my time working in a career that I had no interest in. I've always wanted to follow my passion of health and nutrition, but never followed through. It was during this time that I found myself most uneasy with my job and wanting out. At the same time, I kept seeing hummingbirds. These hummingbirds were everywhere, and they would hover in front of my face for a few minutes or so. I knew this had to be a sign from my guides. This combined with my hesitation to continue a career that was no longer serving me, was an undeniable pull from the universe. I knew my guides were telling me that there's something bigger that needs my attention. Eventually, this shift led me to leave my career to write this book. The universe was sending me a message that it's time to share my struggles, and help others overcome their anxiety.

3. **Animals** are a great form of communication with the other side. You can request that answers come in the form of animals, as I did with the deer and butterfly. Or you can interpret an animal that you encounter symbolically. Before my recent ex-boyfriend

149

and I permanently separated, we met for a walk along the San Francisco Bay. He asked if I thought we were making a mistake by ending things, and I couldn't help but wonder if this was the wrong decision. Suddenly, I noticed a tiny little owl perched on a rock close to the water. It was staring straight at us. It's very rare to see an owl during the day, which is what drew my attention. At the time, I didn't know what the symbolism was, but I knew that the owl being there was no coincidence. At the end of the walk, we decided to part ways for good. Later that night, I researched the symbolism of an owl, and surely enough, it was associated with intuition and change. This was an obvious sign that my intuition was on point, and the breakup was necessary to facilitate change in my life.

4. **Sequence of numbers**, especially when they come in threes. For example, 111 relates to manifestation, which could indicate that your actions and thoughts are aligned with your desires. 222 relates to being in the present moment. 333 relates to being in balance. 444 is a sign that you're being guided. 555 can indicate change is coming. 666 should be taken as a wakeup call that change may be necessary. 777 relates to relinquishing control. 888 indicates that you're on the right track, and 999 is a sign that something is coming to an end.

5. **Songs / lyrics** that randomly pop in your head or start playing on the radio, while you're thinking of something specific. Especially oldies or songs you haven't heard in a while. Think about something you may have asked your guides or what you may have been thinking about when the song appeared. Read the lyrics and determine whether there's symbolism behind the song's title or words.

6. **Dreams** can be used as a means of communication, especially for loved ones who have passed on. In order to listen or feel the energy of the other side, we need to quiet our conscious mind, while activating our unconscious mind. When in a dream state, our conscious mind is deactivated, which makes it easier for our spirit guides to communicate with us. Another reason why the

other side would communicate with us through dreams, rather than while we are awake, is because they don't want to scare us. Highly evolved guides are gentle, loving, and compassionate beings that only want the best for us. The last thing they want to do is scare us. If you find yourself scared in the presence of a guide, then ask them to leave and don't pay any attention to them. They may be a less evolved being, which you don't want to give your energy to.

7. **Recurring names, words or objects** can be an indication that your guides are sending you a message. A name that keeps recurring could be the name of your guide or a loved one that has passed on. They may be trying to tell you that they are with you and guiding you. Repeatedly hearing or seeing words could indicate that your guides are trying to send you a message. Finding or breaking objects can be a sign that you are either on the right or wrong track. Sometimes when I find myself fighting my intuition or repetitively doing something that is serving me in a negative way, something will break. It usually turns out to be a glass object that suddenly falls out of my hands. There's usually no reason I should have lost my grip, but it just happens. This has happened to me numerous times and it is a powerful method your guides can use to get your attention. Alternatively, when you seamlessly find objects that you are thinking about or looking for, means that your vibrations are aligned with the universal energy, and you are on the right track.

8. **Random encounters** - Have you ever noticed that when you think of someone, they end up calling? Or you end up bumping into them? Or how about when you keep bumping into the same person over and over again? These are not coincidences. They are signs from the universe that your vibrations are running high, and that you're attracting exactly what you are thinking about or need in your life at that moment. If you keep running into the same person, then ask yourself why this might be happening. This relationship might serve you now or at some point in the future. Perhaps they are meant to offer you friendship, strength, support, or guidance. Or they could somehow lead you to your next job or

your future soulmate. Also, consider the fact that you may be needed in this person's life as well. After all, the reason you keep bumping into each other is because both of your vibrations are in sync.

Messages from the other side can be delivered in many different ways. It just requires an open mind so that you are aware of the possible forms that the messages can appear in. Don't get discouraged if you find that you're having a hard time communicating with your guides. They are always present and always guiding you, whether it's obvious or not. You may need to pay closer attention to potential signs that are going unnoticed. Guides don't like to scare you, and they may be testing you to see how much you can handle without provoking fear. If they find that they are causing you any fear, they will back off and only use gentle signs, which will require extra attention. Remember to have patience, because guides work on their own time, and it's up to them to decide when you are ready to receive.

Intuition or Anxiety?

I want to emphasize the difference between intuition and anxiety. Spirituality can help you become more intuitive, which can help steer you away from irrational fears. You may think that your fears are some type of premonition, but there is a big difference between intuition and anxiety. Intuition comes to us when we are in a calm relaxed state. It's that silent gentle little inkling in the pit of your stomach, and It's clear, reasonable, and rational. Intuition does not come from a place of fear, panic, negativity or stress. Anxiety induced fear is based on avoidance and not facing negative situations, while intuition is based on strength, resilience, and the ability to face a negative situation head on. Anxiety is future focused, while intuition is about focusing on the present moment.

A good way to listen to your intuition is by meditating. This will bring you into the calm relaxed state that you need to be in, in order to tap into it. Take flying for example. Let's say you're having intense anxiety about a business trip flight, and you have a feeling that something terrible is going to happen. Take a moment and understand that this feeling you are having is not coming from intuition, it is coming from fear-based anxiety. Try your best to calm yourself down by taking long deep breaths. Close your eyes and continue to breathe until you find yourself in a relaxed state. Now you can ask yourself if you really think something bad is going to happen. Something deep in your gut might be telling you that there's a good chance that nothing bad is going to happen.

Picking up on signs will strengthen your faith, as well as your bond with your guide, which will increase your energetic flow with the universe. Now that I have a full understanding of metaphysics and how it's associated with the spiritual world, my faith has been stronger than ever. I no longer fear death or think of death as darkness and nothingness, as I once did when I was a little girl. God, The Universe, whatever you want to call it, is an undeniable energetic force within us and surrounding us. This force is guiding us and supporting us throughout our lives, ready to welcome us with open arms. I wasn't able to comprehend this concept as a little girl, which is what left me hopeless. I now understand that we all have guides that we can turn to in times of need, who are ready and willing to guide us in the right direction. The other side is filled with love, and they only want good things for us. There is no hate, there is no jealousy, there is no disappointment. There is just infinite love.

We all have access to these loving guides, so why should we suffer trying to fix things ourselves, when we can simply ask, be patient, and receive. When your guide feels that you are ready, they will make themselves heard, trust me! The guidance will be undeniably crystal clear, and your guides will be more than willing to help you pick up the pieces in your life. You just need to believe and have faith! There is no need to worry when you have faith. Everything will just fall into place, as long as you allow your energy to flow with the universe. The key to attracting the things you want in life is living your life passionately and joyfully. Think about that. Isn't that amazing? All the Universe wants you to do, is set your intentions, live life joyfully, and openly receive what you ask for. How much more beautiful can it get?

Know that there is a life beyond death, filled with an abundance of love and happiness. There is no fear, there is no anxiety, there is no suffering, it is pure bliss. The idea of knowing that my spirit will live on and that we are just temporary visitors walking this earth gives me peace. We will all transition over to eternal love and happiness at some point, so what is the sense of spending our time worrying here on earth, when it is only temporary?

The Law of Attraction

Sometimes we can't control what situations are dealt to us, but we can control our reactions to those events. Those who think more positively, tend to attract more positive occurrences, while those who think more negatively, tend to attract more negative occurrences. This is called the "law of attraction" which is a derivative from the philosophy of metaphysics. Metaphysics looks beyond the physical world or human sense perception, exploring the spiritual aspects of the world, with an emphasis on mind over matter. Just because we cannot see things, does not mean they don't exist. Manifesting what you want or what you don't want begins with a conscious thought that makes its way into your subconscious mind. Your subconscious thoughts and beliefs create actions that energetically attract like-minded people, things, or circumstances. If you want to attract what you desire, you need to really believe that you can achieve this, despite how unrealistic it may seem. Any doubts put forward only creates resistance toward attracting what you truly desire.

Think of the minerals that create a magnetic pull, such as iron and copper. When an electrical current runs through these two minerals it creates a magnetic force. The human body requires iron and copper to survive, while our cells conduct electrical currents. So biologically, there is a magnetic component to us. Magnetic energy creates a vibrational frequency, which is a result of our thoughts and emotions. We all know that the Earth consists of a magnetic field, which is why a compass can locate the North and South pole from any location on Earth. Isn't that amazing? There's magnetic energy flowing within us and around us at all times. So, why discount the possibility of having the capacity of attracting what we want in our lives?

If you find it challenging to maintain the thoughts that will align you with your true desires, then I'd recommend starting out with planting the seed, having faith, and living your life joyfully along the way. There is significance to the quote, "it's about the journey, not the destination." If you are enjoying the journey while working toward your desires, then everything will fall into place exactly how it needs to be. If our thoughts and emotions are aligned with external forces that are on the same vibrational frequency, they will attract one another.

But sometimes we are in such a negative head space, which makes it seem almost impossible to shift our negative thoughts. There was a time when I found myself so deep in my negative thoughts, that feeling at all positive felt hopeless. This is when I came across the teachings of Esther Hicks, also known as Abraham Hick, who is a powerful spiritual figure. Abraham, a spiritual being who speaks through Esther, considers themselves as a collective group of consciousness from beyond this physical world. Abraham explains that the feelings of love, exhilaration, and joy you experience represents the presence of them within you. When you are feeling these high vibrational emotions, you are aligned with the divine source energy of the universe and are on the way to manifesting whatever it is you really want. In Esther's book, "The Law of Attraction" she emphasizes how energetically powerful it is to live every moment of your life joyfully and how we can work our way up the emotional scale to reach these high vibrations.

Emotional Scale

Joy / Appreciation / Empowerment / Freedom/ Love
Passion
Enthusiasm / Eagerness / Happiness
Positive Expectation / Belief
Optimism
Hopefulness

155

Contentment
Boredom
Pessimism
Frustration / Irritation / Impatience
Overwhelming
Disappointment
Doubt
Worry
Blame
Discouragement
Anger
Revenge
Hatred / Rage
Jealousy
Insecurity / Guilt / Unworthiness
Fear / Grief / Desperation / Despair / Powerlessness

Use this emotional scale as a benchmark to locate your current emotional state, gradually working your way up to number 1. Number 1 runs at the highest vibrational frequency, while Number 22 runs at the lowest. It's not reasonable to expect yourself to immediately jump from the higher scale to the lower scale, as it is a step-by-step process. If you are feeling more than one emotion at the same time, only consider the most predominant emotion that you are experiencing in that moment. For instance, if your anxiety is making you fearful of certain things in life, you are emitting the lowest vibrational frequency, while only feeling worrisome, would run at a higher vibrational frequency.

When I was in Sedona, I felt terrified once I hiked up to this ledge on Cathedral Rock, which meant I was running at the lowest vibrational frequency. I decided to hike down the mountain, and then gradually worked my way back up, maintaining a comfortable pace, as I slowly adjusted my height tolerance as I went along. By the time I made my way back up to that same ledge, the fear had dissipated enough for me to hang out for a few hours. I was no longer terrified, and I was only experiencing a slightly worrisome tickle in my stomach, which meant that I made my way up the emotional scale, thereby raising my vibrational frequency. Sedona is known as a spiritual town that encompasses energetic vortexes, which are swirling centers of energy, known to heal, transform, and inspire, making it the perfect place to set out intentions, allowing you to manifest what you want. This is why I wanted to make sure that I was running at the highest vibrational frequency possible.

Abraham also talks about being an "allower," which means you allow situations, circumstances, and those around you to be as they are, without judgement or interference. Stop trying to control everything around you, because there's much more power in being an allower. For example, if you are in a traffic jam, allow it to just be as it is without causing a reaction. Don't get frustrated, and act out by honking your horn, or swerving through traffic. This only brings on negativity, which will take you further down the emotional scale. Allow the situation to just be as it is, without interference. Or if your partner is in a bad mood and you find that they are trying to argue with you as a result of it, don't get defensive. Instead, allow them to act as they are. Eventually they will calm down and will most likely be appreciative of the way you handled the situation. They may even feel silly for how they reacted, which will make them think twice next time they start to pick a fight with you. You may also have a friend who is going through a tough time, which makes you feel inclined to offer your advice. In this moment, ask yourself if your opinion is really necessary or if all your friend really needs is to just be heard. If your opinion is not received well, it can cause tension between the two of you, resulting in a negative energetic flow. Maintaining your cool can prevent stress and anxiety while keeping you in a positive mindset, allowing your energy to flow seamlessly with that of the universe.

Another way of maintaining a higher vibration is by using the words, "I AM." There is an immense power in the words, "I AM." Repeating this mantra often, followed by what you desire, can alter your brain, causing you to genuinely believe you are truly worthy of manifesting this desire. You can say the following:

"I AM powerful and strong"

"I AM free of anxiety"
"I AM worthy of manifesting whatever it is that I want"
"I AM love, joy and happiness"

Say it with conviction, because you really want to believe and embody these words.

I constantly have my eyes open for signs and guidance. I never go against my gut feeling. I let life flow, welcoming anything that comes into my life, good or bad. I know that the universe is constantly molding and making room in my life for better things to come along. Everything that is happening to me right now is exactly how it's supposed to be, as long as I don't fight it, and I remain joyful along the way. I've finally chosen faith over fear, and I'm the happiest I've ever been. I now walk-through life fearlessly, knowing that the universe has me covered. I trust that I'm being protected and guided in a loving way. Anxiety is based on fear, and fear goes against faith, because having faith means that you trust in the process. Surrender to the universe, and you will learn what true happiness really is.

Flow with The Universe

Sometimes we don't realize how our negativity can be affecting our lives. This negativity puts up resistance toward the universal flow, which perpetually brings in more negativity for us. The movie "Yes Man", which stars Jim Carrey, really resonated with me once I saw it several years ago. It's about a guy who's stuck in a rut, secluded in his house, avoiding the world, until he comes across a self-help guru, who challenges him to say "YES" to anything that comes his way. As he starts saying "YES" to everything, you can see his life slowly transforming from negative to positive, which sparked a whole new excitement for him. His life was finally coming together, and he was attracting everything he wanted. This movie is the perfect example of how the universe provides you with exactly what you need, as long as you just get out of the way. Saying "NO" to things that come your way, is only stopping you from receiving what is really meant for you. Stop the "should have, could have, would have" talk, and start to live your life every day as if it were your last. Explore the wonders of the world, and see what life has to offer you.

Life doesn't need to be that difficult, and if you find that it is, you're probably flowing against the universe. Learn to let things go, learn to accept whatever life hands to you, learn to let circumstances play themselves out, and learn to turn struggles into success. Set your intention while disconnecting from the destination and say "YES" more often to surrender to the universe. This will allow you to start living an effortlessly joyful life, which is conducive to receiving what it is that you truly desire!

So, are you in the flow? You will know if you are on the right track if you start experiencing the following signs:

1. **Synchronistic events** such as being in the right place at the right time to receive whatever it is you're looking for, or need, at that point in your life. For example, randomly meeting that exact person you need to meet to further whatever it is you've been working on.

2. **You're passionate about your work** because you've found your purpose in life. Work doesn't feel like a drag, because you're doing what you love and are passionate about it. You make your dreams and ideas happen, rather than just talking about them. You find that things needed to support you come very easily.

3. **You have genuine relationships** with friends or romantic partners that are easy going and lack conflict. You have let go of any toxic relationships that weren't serving your personal growth.

4. **You're at peace** with yourself and are ok with being in solitude.

5. **You feel joyful every day** and find yourself smiling and sending good vibes to those around you. Things don't bother you much, because you've learned to be an "allower" rather than a "controller." You find that you're turning any obstacles into opportunities with ease.

6. **People are drawn to** you because you speak effortlessly, with wit and wisdom. Those around you actually want to hear what you have to say and are ready to support you with anything you need.

Quantum Physics and Vibrational Energy

To apply and know the law attraction on a deeper level, we must understand Quantum Physics. This science proves that everything emits energy, including humans. Everything in us and around us, is in constant energetic motion, vibrating at various frequencies. Humans are constantly vibrating, emitting, and circulating energy around us. Think of your heartbeat, your breathing, your digestive system, and how they function automatically, which you are able to physically see and feel. We are even vibrating on a cellular level, which is a level we cannot see or feel. The Earth itself also emits certain electromagnetic vibrations. Even stationary objects like rocks or a glass of water are vibrating at various frequencies. Just because we cannot see this vibrating energy, doesn't mean it's not there. When a vibration is triggered, it sets off movement in the surrounding air molecules, which then sets off more air molecules, causing them to vibrate as well. These vibrating air molecules can run at different frequencies, however when they are close enough, they can sync up to start vibrating at the same frequency.

Have you ever walked into a room that was bursting with positive energy? You may have noticed that the energy made you feel really good, which actually fueled your own positive energy. Or how about a time where you walked into a room filled with negative energy, which suddenly made you feel down and heavy. Maybe it even triggered your anxiety. Well, these are high vibrations and low vibrations, and they are contagious when you tune into them. Think back to the emotional scale. Joy / Appreciation / Empowerment / Freedom / Love, runs at the highest vibrational frequency, while Fear / Grief / Desperation / Despair / Powerlessness, runs at the lowest vibrational frequency. Depending on what frequency you're tuned into, you'll attract more of that same frequency.

Television and music give off certain frequencies that you tune into. Someone who runs at the lower end of the emotional scale will likely tune into negative channels, which fuels their negative energy by accumulating more low vibrations. On the other hand, someone who runs on the higher end of the emotional scale would tune into more positive channels that run at higher vibrations. The higher the vibrations you tune into, the more you will attract similar vibrations running at the same frequency. Think of it like the more positive energy you tune into, the more positivity you are accumulating. The more you accumulate, the stronger it gets, and the more you attract what you want in life, because those things are running at the same vibrational frequencies.

Now think about how different genres of music make you feel on an emotional level. When you want to focus, you may turn on classical music, or if you want to feel more energetic, you might turn on dance music. If you listen to the music long enough, your emotions will start to sync up with the sounds you're hearing. This sound is energy created by vibrations running at specific frequencies.

Now consider how our thoughts are affected by what's happening around us. When you think of a stressful thought like how much work you need to do tomorrow, what happens to your body? You may experience muscle tension, and your body will begin to release stress hormones. These bodily reactions are a source of vibrational energy, which your mind created with just one thought. So, if our thoughts can create vibrations, and vibrational energy is known to sync up with similar vibrations, then our thoughts are capable of attracting vibrations on similar frequencies.

Have you ever seen a swarm of birds twisting and whipping around, creating swirling patterns throughout the sky? Well, if you haven't, it's called murmuration, and it involves hundreds or even thousands of starling birds that fly in perfect unison, while swooping, diving, and wheeling themselves in the sky. Isn't that wild? How the heck do these birds fly so perfectly in sync with one another, without coordinating any of their moves beforehand? How do they not crash into each other? This cannot be logically explained on a human level, so it must mean that these birds are somehow connected on an energetic level, vibrating at the same frequency.

How about the game, "Light as a Feather, Stiff as Board?" If you grew up in the 90's, then you most likely played this game. Did you find yourself perplexed at the idea that 4 - 5 girls were lifting a 90-pound girl with just their two fingers? Maybe so, maybe not, but it's undeniable that an exchange of built-up energy is at play here. If you haven't heard of the game, it requires one girl to either lie down, or sit in a chair, while 4 - 5 girls try to lift her with their two fingers. The girls doing the lifting put their hands over the girls' head. They build up energy by rubbing all their hands together, and then keep them over her head for a few minutes. Then they put their two fingers underneath her body and begin to lift her in the air.

I always tried to make sense of this game and I knew that there was significance to holding our hands over the seated girl's head. The girls doing the lifting could be absorbing the energy from the seated girl, which gives them more energy to lift her with just their two fingers. The seated girl could also be absorbing the built-up energy, which enables her to help them lift herself with just her thoughts.

This game can simply be shrugged off by most, but I believe that mental energy, as well as manifestation, is at play here. Could it be that the collective energy absorbed by the seated girl was enough for her thoughts to become physical actions? The seated girl is so focused on levitating that it actually happens, because she's accumulated enough energy from the other girls to make it happen.

Whether you believe in the law of attraction or not, it's undeniable that everything around us emits energy at certain frequencies. This is why it's so important to run at higher energetic vibrations. The higher your vibes, the more you will attract similar vibes running on the same frequency. Your thoughts are very powerful, and they emit energy, so you must be conscious of what you are putting out there, because the energy you put out will be matched with the energy you receive.

Tuning Forks

Tuning forks are known to help alter the frequency that someone is vibrating at. Electromagnetic vibrations are made of either light waves or sound waves. While light waves can travel through empty space, sound waves need air or water to emit sound. This is why there is no sound when an astronaut talks or screams in outer space. Tuning forks use sound vibrations for healing, and sound waves that are transferred through water create stronger vibrations than if they are transferred through air. Humans are 70% water, making tuning forks the perfect means of emitting healing vibrational frequencies.

Any illnesses or disease in the body will cause the vibrational frequency to go out of balance, either running too fast or too slow. Sometimes we need assistance in getting these vibrations back into balance. Think of a guitar that is out of tune and how the song you are trying to play may not sound right as a result of it. It's the same idea for the human body. Sometimes our vibrations need to be tuned up.

Tuning forks can be used to generate sound waves, which can be purchased online for around $15. Emitting sound at a certain pitch, near the imbalance part of the body, can bring that area back into balance. The vibrational frequency being emitted at that particular point of the body, whether too high or too low, will sync up to the frequency being emitted by the tuning forks. You can start out by lightly tapping the fork near the point of imbalance, which can be repeated as necessary. Adjust the strength of the tap to what feels and sounds comfortable. If you are looking for relief from anxiety or any other mental health issue, you can start by strengthening your vagal tone, as most anxious people have a weak vagal tone. This can be done by holding and tapping the tuning fork at the sole of the foot, in an area known as Kidney One in acupressure. Find your middle toe and go down about 2 inches, which is where you can find Kidney One. You can also tap the tuning fork at any other acupressure point known to relieve anxiety. If you don't feel comfortable using tuning forks on yourself, you can always find a clinic to have it professionally done.

Chapter 9: In a Nutshell

1. Let faith take over fear by knowing that the universe loves and supports you. Know that your spirit will live on and life beyond death is nothing but love and eternal happiness.

2. All of us are capable of accessing our spirit guides and they are always ready to offer their guidance when asked.

3. The other side is guiding us every day, however saying "NO" to things that come your way is only putting up resistance to the universal flow. Saying "YES" more often allows you to receive exactly what is meant for you.

4. We are surrounded by energy and magnetic forces, so why discount the possibility that we can attract exactly what we want into our lives. All we need to do is put our intentions out there, really believe that we can achieve it, and live life joyfully along the way.

Chapter 10: Lifestyle

Finding Happiness in The Present Moment

It's so easy to get caught up with the hustle and bustle of everyday life. As humans, we always feel like nothing is ever enough. We seek more money, more material things, more adventures, more experiences, and more lust. It's a constant perpetual chase to the finish line, except we keep going in circles like a hamster on a wheel. Sometimes it takes hitting rock bottom in order to wake up. We must realize that happiness should come from within, not external sources. You cannot rely on anyone else or any material objects to bring you happiness. Everything comes with an expiration date, and if your happiness is based on something that has expired, you're screwed! Happiness that comes from within is everlasting. This is why hitting rock bottom might be the best thing that happens to you. Rather than looking at rock bottom as an obstacle, see it as an opportunity to reflect, learn, and grow. It's during this time that your mind is open, and willing to try anything to get better. This is usually when people are starving for a change, and they seek the spiritual guidance that they so desperately need. The universe will guide you to your spiritual path when they believe you are ready.

When I hit rock bottom, the only thing I wanted to do was sit in nature. I would gaze out into the beauty for hours on end. There was something so peaceful about the birds chirping, the squirrels racing around, and the stillness of the trees. Nature helps us experience the present moment, connecting us to our true selves, which goes way beyond our physical bodies. It was at this point that I started questioning true happiness and the meaning of life, because how I had been living was definitely not it! Being an anxious person, I was always concerned with the future, never living in the present moment. It was at this time that I found "A New Earth" by Eckhart Tolle, which changed my whole outlook on life. He explains how everyone unconsciously operates on ego, which is the very thing that's holding us back from finding true happiness. He emphasizes the importance of the present moment, which is the only thing that really matters, being that yesterday is history, and the future isn't guaranteed. People, material things, adventures, experiences (good or bad), they all come and go. Let go of attachments to external things, because nothing is permanent in life except for your spiritual self.

I felt as though I had been walking around unconscious up until that moment. His quote that really resonated with me was "this too will pass," meaning that any situation you are in (good or bad) is never permanent. Happiness, sadness, joy, fear, anger, they will all eventually subside. This quote can help you when you're experiencing a tough time in life. It can also serve as a wakeup call when you find that you are attaching your happiness to an external factor. Instead, you should find peace and contentment in the present moment, which could be cooking, working, walking, driving, or simply just "being". There is a profound power in stillness, which brings peace, and with peace comes happiness. I found myself constantly smiling and humming throughout the day, genuinely enjoying every moment. Walking my dog every morning, I feel grateful to be breathing the beautiful fresh air, while surrounded by nature's beauty. If you ever need to find balance, let nature heal you by bringing you back to your roots. It really is the simplest things in life that genuinely bring you happiness.

Mindfulness

"Some people feel the rain. Others just get wet." - Bob Marley

It's important to live in the present moment in order to be in a state of peace. Up until now, we've learned that stress fuels the bossy brain. We need to relax ourselves enough to rid our body of the excessive stress hormones that are triggering our "fight or flight" response. People who are carrying around emotional baggage are prisoners of their past. If you are living in the past, you are depressed. Depression fuels the bossy brain, so we need to overcome, acknowledge, and heal our emotional past in order to live in the present moment. Spirituality can help us find ourselves, which can awaken us to our inner happiness. This can only be achieved by learning to live in the present moment. Simply being mindful of our thoughts and actions, can retrain our brain to live in the present.

Mindfulness is the practice of being in the present moment. Practicing mindfulness can increase self-awareness, allowing you to tune into your thoughts, emotions, and body sensations.

Being aware of your thoughts brings you to the present moment. Are your thoughts negative or positive? Are you thinking about the past, future, or present? If you find that you often think negatively or find yourself concerned with the future, then take the time to acknowledge these thoughts when they come in. Simply acknowledging when you have a negative thought can help bring you back into the present moment. Eventually, the more you catch yourself when thinking negatively, the less intrusive those thoughts will become. You can essentially rewire your brain to think more positively by simply acknowledging negative thoughts when they come in. The same goes for future thinking. The more you acknowledge when you have thoughts about the future, the more you will be in the present moment. Acknowledgment of thoughts is a strategy to bring yourself into the present moment. This isn't to say that thinking about the future is a bad thing, but there is a time and place for future thinking. The majority of your time should be spent being in the present moment. You can set aside a time to think about future goals, opportunities, or a trip that you're looking forward to. However, don't dismiss the present moment by constantly thinking about these future events.

Another approach to bring yourself into the present moment is by focusing on your breath. Focusing on your breath moving around within you, can bring attention to thoughts, emotions, and sensations throughout the body. By doing this, you can shift your attention to your body, rather than your bossy brain. Try to get in tune with your senses by deep breathing. Your senses are extremely heightened when your bossy brain is in control, so try to focus on what's around you, rather than the panic you are experiencing. Observe your surroundings, smell the air, physically touch things that you can see. This should help you grasp a sense of reality again, while distracting you from your bossy brain.

Meditation

Meditation stimulates the pituitary gland, which releases oxytocin, dopamine, serotonin, and endorphins. These are all the happy chemicals we need to help keep our bossy brain in check. You can experience numerous benefits by practicing mindfulness meditation for 10 minutes per day. Some benefits include stress reduction, anxiety reduction, lowered blood pressure, improved focus, sleep, learning, memory, and much more.

Take 10 minutes out of your day. All this meditation requires is that you focus on breathing and relaxing your body. If thoughts come into your mind, release them and redirect your focus back to your breathing. Eventually, you'll be able rewire your brain to limit intrusive thoughts, improve memory, concentration and focus. A clearer mind gives you a better chance to get in control of your bossy brain. Studies show that 10 minutes of mindfulness meditation per day for 8 weeks can literally change the shape of your brain.

So many of us are distracted by intrusive thoughts, multi-tasking, worrying about the future, and dwelling about the past, which are all things that fuel the bossy brain. Mindfulness meditation can help improve focus, so that you're able to focus on one thing at a time. It can also improve sleep by helping you focus on the present moment. Meditation can also provide you with tools to help you deal with stressful situations. I get that sometimes it's hard to meditate when your bossy brain has taken control. Your mind and heart might be racing while thinking of multiple things at once. Take a few deep breaths, try your best to calm down, and try any of the following techniques.

1. **Take it one step at a time** - Stop trying to tackle multiple things at once. Try to focus on one thing at a time, preferably a simple task that can be resolved easily. It would be great if you can make a list of everything you're worrying about. Try to justify whether your worries are legitimate or not and how you can resolve them. This should be a time when you evaluate how rational your thoughts currently are. Is it necessary for you to be having these thoughts? Is there an immediate threat associated with these thoughts? If so, then let yourself tackle them one at a time. If not, then let them go or set it aside to deal with at some point in the future.

2. **Immerse yourself in nature** - If possible, take yourself outside or into nature. Take a walk or go for a run. Try to divert your attention to the beauty of the world around you. Focus on the sky, the clouds, the trees, the flowers, the birds, the stars, or the moon. Find peace and safety in nature. Remember that the universe is a loving place and is very supportive of you.

3. **Distractions** - If you can't distract yourself with deep breathing, then try distracting yourself by tackling a task around the house like cooking, cleaning, gardening, or fixing something.

4. **Focus on your breathing** - If being active seems to amplify your anxiety, then find a comfortable, quiet, safe place to lay down. Close your eyes, and focus on deep breathing, which should help bring you back to a relaxed state.

Virtual Reality Meditation

VR for meditation can be used to promote relaxation by immersing yourself in a relaxing environment with peaceful sounds. Some settings would include the ocean, waterfalls, a view, the sky, or anywhere else you find that brings you relaxation and eliminates stress. Incorporating a 10 – 20 minute meditation each day can significantly reduce your stress levels. Eliminating our body of stress and stress hormones is so important in overcoming anxiety.

You can purchase a VR headset for a few hundred dollars and buy different meditation programs of your choice. We already explored VR exposure therapy for facing your fears in the Expose Yourself Chapter. Therefore, you can use the VR headset interchangeably to expose yourself to your fears, as well as promote relaxation. Just to recap, exposure therapy is designed to diminish your fear by repeatedly exposing yourself to your feared scenario.

Acupressure - 6 Pressure Points for Stress and Anxiety Relief

Acupressure can be used as temporary relief for anxiety and stress. If you feel these symptoms developing, try any of the following 6 pressure points. The added benefit of using pressure points right before or during a panic attack is that you can divert your focus from your anxiety to these pressure points.

1. **Hall of Impression** - The point is located between your eyebrows. Apply pressure in a circular motion for 5 - 10 minutes.

2. **Heavenly Gate** - Located in the upper inner shell of your ear. Apply pressure in a circular motion for 2 minutes.

3. **Shoulder Well** - Located in your shoulder muscles. You can pinch this point with your middle finger and your thumb. Apply firm pressure and massage the point for 4 - 5 seconds while you release the pinch.

4. **Union Valley** - Located in the webbing area of your hand between the thumb and index finger. Pinch this point with your index finger and thumb. Massage the point for 4 - 5 seconds while you release the pinch.

5. **Great Surge** - Located on the foot right between the big toe, and the innermost toe. The point is located in the hollow just above the bone. Apply firm pressure and massage for 4 - 5 seconds while you release the pinch.

6. **Inner Frontier Gate** - Located on your inner arm about 1.5 inches before your wrist begins. Apply pressure and massage for 4 - 5 seconds while you release the pinch.

Live Your Life on Purpose

All of us were given a purpose in life, and I mean EVERYONE. There are no exceptions! Purpose can be identified by finding out what your true passions are. What interests you? If nothing interests you now, what interests did you have as a child? What made you feel alive and happy? Purpose is also associated with struggles you may have experienced in life. Have you overcome these struggles? Were you successful in overcoming these struggles? Can you help others overcome these same struggles? A big part of your purpose is giving back to the greater good and helping others. It's absolutely ok to be monetarily motivated, but a lot of your motivation should come from the desire to help others. This is when you know your purpose is coming from a good place and will produce the most gratification. Living out your purpose brings you joy, while helping others can be extremely rewarding. By working toward your purpose, you'll be less stressed out and more motivated to work harder because there is passion involved in your work. A lot of us find ourselves in careers that we are unhappy with, working way too many hours and stressing out as a result of it. This leaves little time or energy to find or work toward our real purpose in life.

At 35 years old, I found myself newly single and in a career that was no longer serving me, which left me feeling unhappy and unfulfilled. I felt defeated, lost, confused, and lacking direction. I was yearning for something more meaningful in life, something that would speak to my soul, but I didn't know what that was. This feeling of the unknown was uncomfortably foreign to me. During this time, my friend randomly sent me a clip of Oprah Winfrey speaking on purpose. In this video, Oprah talks about how we must live our lives with purpose. This short 2-minute video clip was so unbelievably powerful, yet I didn't understand the meaning behind it or even believe I had a purpose. I had always associated purpose with my goals and future achievements, but I told myself, this couldn't be what she was talking about because those things weren't fulfilling me anymore. I researched what life's purpose meant and realized Oprah was speaking on finding your passion, and what really makes your heart sing. She was talking about living life passionately every single day.

I knew that health and nutrition was always something I had been passionate about. I didn't know how I would be able to incorporate this into my career, being that I had been in finance for the past 12 years. This left me feeling just as confused as before. So, I set myself on a purpose driven journey and put my intentions out into the universe. Throughout the next few months, I would brainstorm ideas and constantly talk about finding my purpose. I researched articles on finding purpose, watched videos, and read books to get some general direction. One day, my friend and I hiked up Runyon Canyon in Los Angeles, which is a beautiful hike that leads you up the mountain to a gorgeous view of the city. We stood there taking in the view while talking about our dreams and passions. I told her how determined I was to find my purpose and that I would never go back to my old career again. There was something so powerful in that moment that we shared together, that I knew I would be finding my purpose very soon.

About a week after the hike, I was reading Rick Warren's book, "The Purpose Driven Life" when it suddenly hit me. He spoke of God given talents, overcoming struggles in life, and how you should help others with the same struggles you've experienced. I now knew helping others overcome anxiety was going to be my purpose in life. I've suffered from anxiety for 18 years but have been anxiety free for over 10 years now. I have so much to share, and I have a burning desire to help those suffering from the same thing. I was able to incorporate health and nutrition as anxiety is deeply rooted in it. I had finally put the puzzle together and I knew this is why I was put here on earth.

It's no accident that I discovered my purpose at the time that I did. Life's challenges indicate that a change is needed, which is the universe's way of guiding you in the right direction. Without struggles, there would be no opportunity for self-growth. A lot of people get caught up in the hustle and bustle of everyday life, just trying to survive. We forget how beautiful life is, and don't realize that we are capable of experiencing happiness and joy, every single day. Why spend every day of your life tirelessly and endlessly working at a career that is leaving you feeling unfulfilled, when you can find your true purpose, which is guaranteed to make you thrive. Anxiety is fueled by fear and a lack of trust. Discovering who you really are at the core will return your sense of security. If you feel like the universe is giving you a nudge, take the time to stop, listen, and reflect. Let yourself explore your purpose here on earth and who you really are at the core of your being.

Creatures of Habit

Fearful thoughts, anticipation, and a fear of the unknown fuels the bossy brain. Anxious people find comfort in familiarity, so having a routine can help you gain more control over your life, which brings a sense of security. It will also distract you from having intrusive thoughts throughout the day, as you'll be focused on tackling and completing each task with little distractions. Humans are creatures of habit, which is why we thrive in an environment conducive to structure and organization. Having a daily routine can help alleviate stress, improve eating habits, sleep, and exercise habits, while creating more time for your day. Here are some ideas to help jump start your daily routine.

Routine Ideas

1. **Starting your day with a quick meditation** can help you feel relaxed, clear headed and focused. You may find it easier to

meditate in the morning, because you won't have a ton of thoughts going through your mind yet.

2. **Take a moment to plan out your day**. Having a plan will help you eliminate unexpected obstacles, while allowing you to utilize your time more efficiently.

3. **Have your morning tea, coffee, or warm lemon water**. If you have an outdoor space, I suggest enjoying your warm beverage outdoors. This will help you get in tune with nature, which will help keep you centered and relaxed throughout the day. You can take this time to plan out your day or take this time to stay present, while enjoying nature's beauty. You'll most likely be spending most of your day indoors, so enjoy this moment by taking in the fresh air and have gratitude for this beautiful day. Being grateful each day will help align you with the flow of the universe, which keeps you on the path to receiving what you really want in life.

4. **Meal prepping in the morning or at night** can help you eat better. Waiting until you're hungry to cook might deter you from choosing a healthier meal. You may end up grabbing that bag of chips or cookies that you could have avoided otherwise. This is also a great way to incorporate a daily juice, smoothie or wheatgrass shot. Preparing these ahead of time will ensure that you are able to squeeze one in every day.

5. **Set time aside for exercise** at some point during the day. Exercise is crucial for those with anxiety, because we need all the happy chemicals we can get. At the very least, set aside time each day for some type of physical activity, even if it's just a short walk.

6. **Get 7- 8 hours of sleep**, in which you sleep and wake at the same time each day. I would recommend trying to go to sleep around 10 pm, because this will allow you more time in the morning so that you stick with your daily routine. Waking up early allows you to get more done, leaving you with more time later in the day to focus on yourself.

7. **Set aside some time to focus on something creative, a hobby, your passion project**, or anything that brings you joy and excitement. Doing things that brings us happiness from within gives us a sense of purpose in life. Prioritizing time for these activities will help keep us focused on living our life purposefully each day.

8. **Commit to a charitable organization or do something that involves giving back to society**. Sometimes giving has greater benefits than receiving, because helping others can feel really rewarding. It also gives you a sense of purpose, boosts your self-worth, and helps distract you from your bossy brain. You can even start small by making a habit of doing one "act of kindness" each day.

9. **Journaling** can be very therapeutic, because it's a way to express your thoughts and release stagnant emotions. Journaling can be a stress reliever, as well as a way to examine, work through, and shift anxious thoughts to more empowering ones. You can shift your thought process by writing down your anxious feelings and rephrasing those feelings in a more empowering way. The more you do this, the more automatic these feelings of power and strength will become.

Prioritize your morning routine, because how you feel in the morning usually sets the tone for the rest of your day. Sticking with your morning routine will help the rest of your day fall into place, increasing your likelihood of succeeding with your daily routine. If you can manage to maintain your routine for at least 3 weeks, you'll have a higher likelihood of sticking with it. The key is not to put too much pressure on yourself, but to have fun with it. Create a routine tailored to what you enjoy doing with your day, because this is about YOU and what brings you happiness.

Chapter 10: In a Nutshell

1. Happiness that comes from external sources are short lived, while happiness that comes from within is eternal. Tap into that eternal happiness by learning to live in the present moment.

2. Mindfulness is a practice that encourages you to be aware of your thoughts and actions, which will automatically bring you to the present moment.

3. A lot of us get lost in the hustle and bustle of everyday life, feeling unfulfilled, and working at jobs we are unhappy with. All of this provokes unnecessary stress. Living out your purpose is more fulfilling, brings happiness, and even eliminates stress.

4. Having a routine can help eliminate stress and promote a healthy lifestyle. Find what works for you and stick to it!

Chapter 11: Gratitude

Emotional Intelligence and Anxiety

Emotional Intelligence is the ability to acknowledge and manage your own emotions, as well as the emotions of others. These emotions can be positive or negative, consisting of happiness, sadness, excitement, anger, jealousy, and so on.

This might sound counterintuitive, but people with anxiety tend to be more emotionally intelligent than those without anxiety. This is because they are in touch with uncomfortable emotions and tend to be more in tune with their body, feelings, actions, as well as other people, and their surroundings. People with anxiety have irrational worries and fears, which would make it seem like they are less intuitive, but this is not the case when it comes to feeling their emotions and the emotions felt by others. Their intuition regarding other people's feelings is usually on point.

In fact, not only is someone with anxiety more attuned to other people's emotions, but they are actually emotionally affected by them, and have a genuine desire to make others feel better. Most anxious people have a humbleness to them and are empathetic toward other people's emotions. However, this comes at a price, as being around someone who is experiencing negative emotions may actually trigger anxiety for the anxious person. For example, if an anxious person meets up with their friend who is experiencing sadness or anger, the anxious person is likely to take on these emotions themselves. They will attempt to make the other person feel better, because once their friend is feeling better, they will feel better.

Although this type of behavior can be exhausting, those with anxiety tend to cultivate more authentic relationships as a result of it.

The Blessings of the Bossy Brain

It may be tough to see your anxiety as a blessing, but it really could be if you learn to look at it from a different perspective. Looking back on my experience with anxiety, I feel grateful for the effect it had on my life. Having anxiety forced me to live a healthier life, having anxiety forced me to say goodbye to toxic relationships, having anxiety forced me to quit toxic behavior, having anxiety has humbled me, having anxiety has made me more compassionate toward others, having anxiety has made me more self-aware of my actions, having anxiety has motivated me to succeed in life, having anxiety has forced me into personal growth, having anxiety has given me the opportunity to write this book and help others, which I could not have done otherwise.

Research suggests that there is a connection between people with anxiety and higher intelligence. The idea lies in the anxious person's creativity, and the fact that they are constantly trying to analyze everything around them. Picture a robot that's scanning everything around it, in order to access, analyze, and retain information. This is what anxious people do all the time. The downfall is that this intelligence is consumed by a lot of unnecessary information. If you learn how to redirect this intelligence toward something you're passionate about, you will see what I'm talking about. Your brain will go above and beyond to make sure you are successful at what you are focused on!

Limp or Leap

It's up to you to choose whether you're going to limp through life with anxiety or leap through life free and fearlessly! Successfully beating anxiety requires courage, determination, and a burning desire to live an anxiety free life. A lot of people choose to just deal with their anxiety or put little effort into overcoming it, not realizing that there's a way out. Be that person that's not going to take "NO" for an answer. Take control and leap!

80/20 Lifestyle

The key to success and longevity in life is moderation. I believe too much of anything is not healthy, which is why I believe in being healthy 80% of the time, while letting loose 20% of the time. This enables you to live a healthy, fulfilling life, while allowing yourself to have some fun. This will also improve your chances of succeeding, as you will not be completely depriving yourself. Have that glass of wine, eat that piece of pie, skip that day of exercise. As long as you're healthy 80% of the time, these little indulgences shouldn't cause a relapse. If you find that any of these are causing an issue, then leave them out.

My point is, don't be too hard on yourself if you fall off the wagon. Accept that you're human and you're capable of making mistakes. It doesn't matter how many times you fall off, just get right back on and keep moving forward! Living a healthy life is a lifestyle, not a fad, not a diet, and not a competition with others, so don't look at it this way. Think of healthy living as a dark shade of gray, rather than black or white. I encourage you to figure out what your little vices may be and allow yourself to enjoy them every so often.

Chapter 12: Conclusion

I've never had effective experiences with therapists. It seemed maybe they didn't know how to provoke productive conversions, or maybe they dismissed my experiences because they didn't find them to be significantly traumatic. I believe everyone's traumatic experience (big or small) is relative to the person and how it was interpreted by them. When talking with therapists, we would briefly skim over my childhood, followed by long conversations regarding everyday insignificant experiences. At 27 years old, my therapist told me there was nothing else he could do for me. I left that day feeling just as anxious as I did when first started seeing him. I felt defeated, realizing my sad reality of living with anxiety for the rest of my life.

After experiencing repeated panic attacks, I decided enough is enough. I was going to do everything possible to beat this anxiety myself. I started reading articles, books, watching documentaries or anything else related to healing the brain. I read blogs written by others suffering from the same thing, which is what gave me a sense of hope. I couldn't believe that I wasn't the only one experiencing these terrors. People would share their stories and different techniques they used to work through their anxiety. I would try these techniques and realized that some of them actually worked. My panic attacks were becoming less frequent and the fact that I was seeing results motivated me to keep on learning and experimenting.

I then came across an article regarding the correlation between anxiety and poor digestion. This is when it hit me. I knew I had to lead a healthier life by altering my eating habits and lifestyle. I quit smoking cigarettes, significantly cut down on drinking, stopped drinking coffee, started doing yoga, meditating, and became somewhat of a health freak. Smoothies and wheatgrass became my morning ritual, followed by a diet consisting of lots of veggies, nuts, seeds, healthy grains, and lean protein, with an emphasis on raw food. At this point, I noticed my digestion really started to improve. This helped boost my mental performance, creating a healthy headspace for me. I was able to get in control of my irrational thought process. The wheatgrass helped detox my body of any toxins and heavy metals. It also gave me the vitamins and nutrients I was lacking. I had my dentist replace my amalgam cavities with composite to limit my mercury exposure. It was as if a miracle had occurred. I was finally anxiety free!

Looking back, I couldn't understand why my therapists wouldn't recommend any of these techniques or even suggest a healthier nutrition and lifestyle plan. This is not to say all therapists aren't effective, because I believe therapy has come a long way over the last 10 years. All I'm saying is to be picky about your therapist and only go to someone who is in tune with modern concepts and continues to educate themselves in the industry. I also think it's extremely important to take initiative by educating yourself. Research what options you may have and any emerging technologies that could assist you in your recovery. You can utilize these techniques or equipment at home or find a clinic that offers them as a service. Get a blood test to see if you're lacking any essential vitamins or minerals. A healthy gut and proper nutrition are such a fundamental aspect of an optimally functioning brain and body. This is why the mental health industry needs to put more of an emphasis on it.

There's always an underlying source to your symptoms, and that's right, ANXIETY IS A SYMPTOM! Treat your body like an unsolved mystery by figuring out and fixing all the glitches, one by one. Whether it be stagnant unresolved trauma, digestive issues, nutritional deficiency, underlying disease, inflammation, or just educate yourself enough to be able to pinpoint whatever the root cause may be. By understanding what's causing your anxiety, as well as knowing the tools and techniques at your disposal, you can formulate a unique personalized plan to beat it. I encourage you to be your own doctor, because you ARE in control of your body, and it's up to YOU to run it at its full potential!

Expose stagnant emotional trauma, so you can heal and free yourself of this burden you've been carrying around. Blocked emotional trauma disguises and reveals itself through negative emotions like anxiety, depression, irritability, mood swings, sadness, hopelessness, and many other ways. The only way to eliminate stagnant emotional trauma is to identify it, re-experience the emotion, and heal it.

Ego and judgement provoke sadness and separation, while love and presence promotes peace and oneness. Ego builds walls, while humility breaks them down. Allow yourself to be happy and allow others to be themselves. Learn to accept yourself and others for who we all really are. We are all ONE consisting of the same basic elements and emotions. Everybody has a beautiful uniqueness to them and if you don't agree, send them a blessing and walk the other way. We don't need to have an opinion about everything or everybody.

Allowing is so much more powerful than controlling. Release resistance and let the universal energy flow through your life freely. Learn, listen, connect, share; these are the essence to building positive relationships. Living a judgement free life allows you to be happy, which enables the universe to deliver what your heart truly desires. Having faith in a higher power gives you courage, excitement, and a burning desire to live life to its fullest. Set your intentions and continue to live your life joyfully. Remember that it's the journey, not the destination, so you must trust that the universe will deliver in her own way, on her own time, and you will get exactly what it is that you need in life.

About the Author

Taleen Keuftedjian is a mental health and wellness enthusiast who coaches others on the importance of emphasizing modern wellness, which incorporates whole-body health. She takes a relatable approach to mental wellness where she uses her own personal experiences to help motivate others. She lives in San Francisco, California, where she passionately experiences an ultimate zest for life. Her goal is to help others live a healthier, happier, anxiety-free life.

Learn more about Taleen at habitatforwellness.com/about-taleen-keuftedjian/

Explore more mental wellness blogs by Taleen at habitatforwellness.com/blog-wellness-well-being-lifestyle-mental-health-happiness/

Made in the USA
Monee, IL
29 December 2021

87520977R00105

One Last Thing

If you enjoyed this book and found it useful in overcoming your battle with anxiety, I would be extremely grateful if you could take a minute to leave a short review on Amazon. Your support is much appreciated and I'm sending you lots of love and gratitude for your kind words. I read all my reviews personally and I'm excited to hear your thoughts.

Take care and thank you again for your support!